Kilns and Kiln Firing
for the Craft Potter

Kilns and Kiln Firing for the Craft Potter

H. FRASER, L. I. Ceram.

London
Sir Isaac Pitman and Sons Ltd

First published 1969

SIR ISAAC PITMAN AND SONS LTD.
Pitman House, Parker Street, Kingsway, London, W.C.2
Pitman House, Bouverie Street, Carlton, Victoria 3053, Australia
P.O. Box 7721, Johannesburg, Transvaal, S. Africa
P.O. Box 6038, Portal Street, Nairobi, Kenya

PITMAN PUBLISHING CORPORATION
20 East 46th Street, New York, N.Y. 10017

SIR ISAAC PITMAN (CANADA) LTD.
Pitman House, 381-383 Church Street, Toronto

SBN: 273 43692 9

MADE IN GREAT BRITAIN AT THE PITMAN PRESS, BATH
F9—(G.3338)

Foreword

By Henry L. Podmore, B.Sc., F.R.I.C., F.I.Ceram.

Most craft potters are highly skilled in the art of shaping and decorating their particular products, but unfortunately there are many who fail to obtain optimum results from the last, and in some ways the most important, of the series of processes involved—namely, the firing of the finished article.

The correct firing of pottery is not quite so simple as beginners in the craft often believe, but on the other hand, there is no "black magic" in the process. Success in firing mainly comes from an understanding of what happens when ceramic materials are heated, the specific firing requirements of the products and an ability to control the temperature/time cycle and atmosphere of the kiln. Hence the author has wisely concentrated on these fundamental aspects.

The book does, however, cover a large number of related subjects such as the historical development of the kiln, kiln design and construction, accessories and instrumentation, kiln placing and a very useful chapter entitled "Some faults and how to overcome them." The book can, therefore, fairly claim to be comprehensive and as such will not only prove of inestimable value to the craft potter and the pottery teacher, but will also find a useful place on the shelf of the student, the research worker and the industrial ceramist.

The author studied ceramics at the North Staffordshire College of Technology and afterwards spent several years in the pottery industry as a technical manager before becoming captivated by the craft potter's art.

During more recent years he has had much experience in craft pottery and also in the design and production of small craft pottery kilns. Henry Fraser is, therefore, well qualified in his subject and without doubt has succeeded in producing an interesting and informative book that will certainly fill a long-felt need.

Henry L. Podmore
Podmore & Sons Ltd.
Stoke-on-Trent

Preface

There has been a tremendous upsurge in do-it-yourself pottery in the last few years. This coming winter, hundreds of evening institutes in towns and villages all over the country will introduce pottery-making into their curriculum and by so doing will swell the ranks of the thousands whose courses are already well established. The following winter hundreds more will be following in their wake. As a result of this there is a new look about many British homes today: precious family ornaments are being replaced by an assortment of pottery objects, the like of which we may never have seen before. There are heavy, chunky vases, made from coils of terracotta, buff or white clays, piggy-banks decorated with glorious flower patterns, ornate plant-pots, and enough ash-trays to supply the family for years to come.

There is no doubt that there is an immense satisfaction to be gained not merely from creating objects of beauty and value and individuality but from seeing one's skill develop from day to day, as well as the sense of pleasure derived from a job well done. This increasing interest in the ancient craft of potting is very largely attributable to the development of a range of studio electric kilns, firing to high temperatures but at prices to suit all pockets.

Despite the tremendous success with which the long-awaited arrival of the modern studio kiln has been received it still tends to remain something of a mystery to many pupils and teachers—a mysterious magical box of tricks of immense complexity and uncertain operation, seemingly demanding years of experience before satisfactory operation can be achieved. Every kiln firing is viewed with awe, every kiln fireman with wonderment. Many pupils would dearly like to purchase their own kilns to produce pottery in their own homes, but they do not because they dare not, believing as they do that kiln firing is so dreadfully complicated. Nothing could be further from the truth. Kiln firing merely demands a working knowledge of what each switch or knob is for—and these are few in number—coupled with a very basic knowledge of what happens to pottery at each stage of a kiln firing.

This book has been written to supply this knowledge and to enable the complete novice to select the right kiln and to fire his pottery with complete assurance and satisfaction.

There will be much here, too, for the teacher or advanced studio potter, who may find those chapters on kiln instrumentation or kiln evolution of particular interest.

Acknowledgments

My thanks are due to the following companies who have so kindly provided information or photographs used in the compilation of this book—

Podmore & Sons Ltd., Kilns & Furnaces Ltd., Ether Instruments Ltd., Bernard W. E. Webber Ltd., The Metallic Tile Co. (Rowley Bros.) Ltd., A Meakin Ltd., The Carborundum Co. Ltd., British Ceramic Services Co. Ltd., Gibbons Bros. Ltd., Sangamo Weston Ltd., W. T. Copeland & Sons Ltd., Doulton Fine China Ltd., Harrison & Sons Ltd.

Also to the Editors of *A History of Technology* published by the Clarendon Press, Oxford, for permission to reproduce Figs. 1, 2 and 3 and for information about primitive firing methods; to Mr. A. R. Mountford, Director of the City Museum, Hanley, for much information and assistance on the subject of Roman and Medieval kilns; to the North Staffordshire College of Technology for assistance with photographs; and to the College of Earth and Mineral Sciences, Pennsylvania State University for permission to reproduce material from *Fundamentals of Ceramics*.

To Jill

Contents

Illustrations

1 Evolution of the Kiln

Pottery is possibly man's oldest industry. Its origins are probably closely connected with observations made by primeval man thousands upon thousands of years ago of such facts as that footprints or other depressions in a clayey soil hardened in the sun. He could also have observed that depressions in the shade were softer and colder than similar ones exposed to the rays of the sun.

Eventually man mastered fire and scooped primitive hearths out of the earth in which his fires were lit. At Jarno, in the Kurdish foothills, Neolithic basins scooped in the floor had been hardened by fire and there is probably some link between the fortuitous hardening of these hearths and the purposeful firing of clay objects in the open fire for we know that during the last ice age the mammoth-hunters of Vestonice in Moravia constructed hearths at which they hardened images of animals.

We know, by excavational discoveries, that clay products which had been burned in a fire were made in Britain and other parts of Europe some 15,000 years ago. Burned or fired ceramic ware made 13,000 years ago has also been discovered in the Nile valley. This great river continually deposits mud at a constant rate on to the surrounding land, thus raising its level. By measuring the depth at which objects are located below the present level of the valley and relating this to the known rate of mud deposition it is possible to estimate the age of those excavated.

Pottery firing in those days could have consisted of little more than placing the clay pots on the ground and building an open fire around them. By packing wads of fuel on and around the fire and damping them the fire could be made to burn longer, and from these humble beginnings perhaps the first fire was walled in and the oven evolved.

It must not, however, be assumed that the advent of the kiln marked the demise of the open fire; this is very far from the case. Open firing is quite effective up to about 750°C and fuels such as brushwood, grass, and dung could be used which were cheaper than the wood or charcoal necessary for the kiln. It was partly such economic considerations that made it necessary to fire pottery by the open-hearth method in Lewes as late as A.D. 1863. The improved draught control of a kiln gives better results, there is better heat conservation than with the open fire, and higher temperatures can be maintained, but until comparatively recent times more firing was done by open-fire techniques than was done by the use of kilns.

It is, of course, impossible to give precise dates at which processes were developed in ancient history, as the history of pottery is anything but one of constant development. By studying actual discoveries at the sites of ancient temples, tombs, etc., we have, however, been able to learn much about the ancient potter's craft. From pictures on the walls of tombs of the Theban period (3000 to 1700 B.C.), for example, we can see how the Egyptian potter modelled his vases by hand from clay which had been worked to a homogeneous consistency by constant treading and kneading with the bare feet (the same process done by hand we now refer to as "wedging"). The pottery was then placed in the narrow vertical kilns which are characteristic of this period and which were loaded from the top, the top of the kiln being subsequently closed with vegetable matter (*see* Figs. 1, 2, and 3).

These simple vertical kilns were of the updraught type, as were the horizontal kilns which were also in use at this time but which tended to be more popular in the Far East than in more westerly countries.

The Far-Eastern kilns were generally larger and therefore required firing less frequently than those of other areas. The early ones were normally of the horizontal or semi-horizontal type operating on a through draught rather than on the direct updraught principle. One of the big disadvantages of through-draught and updraught kilns is that it is very difficult to baffle back the heat successfully—the flames tend to rush unimpeded through the firing chamber and this is largely responsible for their poor efficiency. The downdraught principle was soon developed, however, and this resulted in considerable fuel savings whilst allowing higher temperatures to be reached and maintained.

A typical Far-Eastern "climbing" downdraught kiln is illustrated in Fig. 4. It will be seen that this consisted largely of a series of downdraught chambers joined together. The lowest

Fig. 1. An Egyptian pottery in the Middle Kingdom, *c.* 1900 B.C.
The narrow vertical kiln is characteristic of the period. From a tomb at Beni Hasan.

Fig. 2. Egyptian pottery of Dynasty V.
The small kiln appears to be closed at the top with a layer of vegetable matter, *c.* 2500 B.C.

Fig. 3. New-Kingdom Egyptian Pottery.
The kiln is of the same type as in Fig. 2. From a tomb at Thebes, *c.* 1450 B.C.

one was fired first, the exhaust gases passing progressively through each chamber, thus preheating them, until the gases emerged from the short chimney or stack built on to the highest chamber. The firing of each kiln was assisted by additional firemouths set in the side of each chamber but by the time the the last two or three chambers came to be fired very little extra heat would have been necessary to reach normal firing temperatures, since the kiln structure and the enclosed pottery would already be very hot because of the products of combustion from the firing of the earlier chambers passing through them.

The downdraught principle was later used to adapt the European vertical updraught kilns to great advantage. The downdraught principle allows the exhaust gases to remain in the kiln for a longer period of time than is the case with the vertical system. The exhaust gases therefore have more time

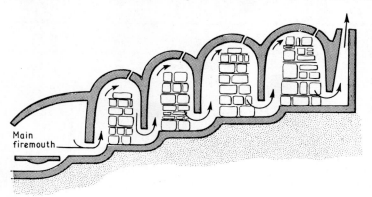

Fig. 4. Far-Eastern climbing downdraught kiln

to give up their heat content to the kiln, ware, etc., and therefore emerge from the kiln at considerably lower temperatures.

A kiln which is heated and then cooled down so that the ware can be removed is called an "intermittent" or "periodic" kiln as distinct from a "continuous" kiln, from which fired pottery emerges continuously rather than in intermittent batches.

All the kilns of this period, and, indeed, up to comparatively recent times, were of the intermittent type, and where kiln firing was carried out the vertical type of intermittent kiln was in much more general usage than the horizontal type.

This was particularly so in Western Europe and several very good examples of the Roman type of vertical intermittent kiln have been excavated. A vertical section and a plan of a typical kiln are shown in Figs. 7 and 8: it will be seen that the kiln is of simple construction consisting basically of a stokehole dug out of the ground and a flue dug under the ground to a firing chamber. A central support in this chamber supported the radiant firebars, invariably made of clay, which served as the hearth of the kiln. The pots were loaded carefully on to the hearth and a domed roof of clay and grass or straw was built

Fig. 5. A primitive vertical kiln

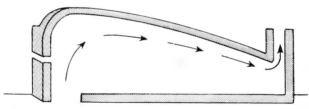

Fig. 6. Horizontal kiln of fire-hardened clay and brick, China, A.D. 100.

around the pots with an aperture left in the top for the escape of smoke, steam, etc. The fuel was loaded from the stokehole into the firemouth, the flames sweeping up the flue, through the hearth, through the load of ware, and out through the hole or holes in the roof.

Fig. 9 is most interesting for this is a photograph of a kiln excavated at Trent Vale, Stoke-on-Trent, and shows the layout of a typical Roman vertical kiln quite plainly. The domed roof, of course, is not shown as this would probably have been destroyed after each firing. Fig. 10, which shows the radiant firebars of this kiln, is also very interesting.

There were many Roman variations of this type of kiln: sometimes a pair of kilns were built radiating from the same

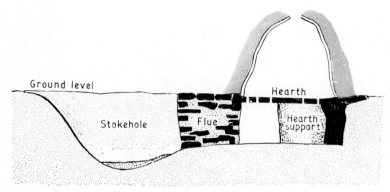

Fig. 7. Roman vertical kiln: vertical section

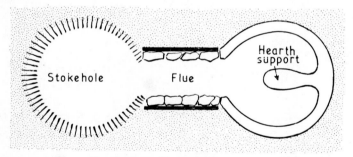

Fig. 8. Roman vertical kiln: plan

stokehole; sometimes the hearth support was permanent, sometimes temporary.

About two tons of fuel (wood) would have been needed to fire such a kiln and the maximum temperature the kiln could attain would be about 960° to 1000°C. There would, however, have been a considerable temperature variation and while certain parts of the kiln might reach 1000°C other parts would probably not rise above 850°C or so.

It would have been far easier for the Romans to transport the fuel rather than the clay or the fired pots. Consequently their kilns tended to be built near to a source of clay or near to a roadway or navigable river rather than near to a source of fuel.

In England this type of kiln continued virtually unchanged for a considerable while and we find that very similar ones were in use many centuries later. It should not, however, be assumed that in England and Western Europe *all* pottery kilns were at this time of the simple updraught type built mainly below ground level. This type certainly appears to have been the most popular—probably because of economic considerations— but there were several variations on this theme and it is known that around the tenth century A.D. many kilns were in use which were based on the Roman design but which had several firemouths feeding the one firing chamber into which the pots were placed.

There is little doubt that the Romans also made use of kilns which were built of brick, etc., above ground and were thus more permanent structures, but kilns such as this do not appear to have been in general use in Europe until medieval times, when we find several well-authenticated references to the sort of kilns used for pottery firing.

In the sixteenth century an Italian named Piccolpasso set down in considerable detail the manner in which pottery was produced. He described not only the processes and the tools used but also gave sketches of the kilns used at that time. Other authentic references are available, some of which refer to kilns having a "round copped form," in which case they would obviously be similar, at least in roof structure, to the Roman ones. Fig. 11, which is a sixteenth-century woodcut, is interesting for this shows a kiln (in the bottom right-hand corner) which appears to have preheating or drying chambers underneath the actual firing chambers.

In the City Museum in Hanley, Stoke-on-Trent, can be seen the base structure of a kiln that was in use about A.D. 1700 and which was located in the grounds of what is now the Albion

Fig. 9. View of Roman kiln excavated at Trent Vale, Stoke-on-Trent

Fig. 10. Firebars of Roman kiln excavated at Trent Vale, 1st century A.D.

Fig. 11. 16th-century woodcut depicting pottery production
(*By courtesy of City Museum, Hanley*)

Hotel in Hanley. This particular kiln, incidentally, was carefully uncovered and removed brick by brick and stone by stone and resited in the Museum grounds by the Stoke-on-Trent Archaeological Society. Each piece was put together *exactly* as it was found; the angle at which each brick was set was very carefully reproduced, the kiln was built facing exactly the same direction and even the thickness of the cement and the positions

Fig. 12. Base structure of kiln in use about A.D. 1700 at Hanley, Stoke-on-Trent

(*By courtesy of City Museum, Hanley*)

of the broken shards, etc., found around the kiln were carefully copied. The kiln is therefore not a replica but a true original and after being hidden for so many generations is now preserved for all to see.

This kiln consists of a central chamber about 8 feet in diameter and has five firemouths arranged around its periphery, together with a single entrance. It is interesting to note that saggars were in use, as is evidenced by those found actually inside the kiln.[1]

[1] Saggars are refractory boxes made of a clay which normally contains a lot of grog. The saggars are then biscuit fired so that they are strong enough to be stacked one above the other. Saggars are still in use today but by no means so extensively as they were some fifty years ago—largely as a result of the development of the continuous tunnel kiln.

Above the kiln base was built a brick dome which was about 8 feet high and probably had a single exhaust hole in the top to let out the products of combustion. The pottery to be fired was therefore carried into the kiln inside saggars which were then placed into position one above the other until the kiln was filled, when the entrance would have been tightly bricked up and the fires started.

The transition from the primitive Roman type of kiln having several firemouths radiating from a central firing chamber is logical and it is obvious that the Hanley kiln is a development of the Roman type, but whereas the Roman kilns were built mainly below ground, the Hanley one was constructed above ground-level with a much more permanent dome.

In the same way that the Roman updraught kiln was the forerunner of the type of kiln found at Hanley so was this type of kiln to be the forerunner of the "bottle" oven which gave such character to the Potteries area of North Staffordshire. Bottle ovens were used very extensively and many different types were produced but the first were probably built around A.D. 1700 and were of the updraught type.

The bottle oven was a very important factor in the development of Stoke-on-Trent as the major pottery-producing area of Great Britain. It is common knowledge, of course, that increasing amounts of pottery were being made in the Stoke-on-Trent area well before the bottle oven became developed to the degree which made it so popular, for many local clays were quite suitable for pottery production. What is not generally realized, however, is that a good-quality coal is needed to obtain the best results from a bottle kiln—a coal that burns with a long flame which can lick up into the kiln and thus give a better heat distribution. There are abundant supplies of this type of fuel in the North Staffordshire area and this fact must have considerably enhanced the appeal of Stoke-on-Trent as an advantageous site for the production of pottery. Eventually there were to be literally thousands of bottle kilns built and operated in the Potteries, which resulted in its unique skyline.

Most bottle ovens consisted basically of two virtually separate structures; the domed roof oven into which the saggars of ware were placed and an outer wall surrounding this and tapering to a hole some two to five feet in diameter at the top. The domed roof oven was referred to as the "hovel" and was built with several firemouths arranged around its side—much like the Hanley type of kiln. The floor of the hovel was raised some two feet or so above ground-level and had a firehole made in the centre so that the heat and flames from each of the

Fig. 13. 18th-century woodcut showing ware being placed in saggars and being carried into a "bottle" oven

firemouths could pass under the floor and pass into the hovel through the firehole. Much of the heat from the firemouths, however, escaped upwards from the firemouths, and thus between the tightly packed saggars and the inside wall of the hovel. To protect the saggars immediately in front of the firemouths from becoming overheated, a protective wall known as a "bag" wall was built, which deflected the heat upwards into the hovel. The hot gases then passed out of the hovel either through a hole in the centre of the domed roof or through vent holes which were arranged around the lower parts of the roof structure. All of these exhaust holes were fitted with covers or dampers, manipulation of which during the firing of the kiln enabled the operator to reduce the rate of temperature increase of certain parts of the kiln while increasing other parts so that a more even temperature distribution could be obtained. Sight-holes were spaced evenly around the kiln so that the fireman could check the colour of the glow and use this to estimate the temperature. The outer wall served to protect the hovel and the firemen from adverse weather conditions, and also created the necessary draught to pull the exhaust gases emanating from the hovel, upwards and out of the kiln to the atmosphere.

At the famous Spode bone china factory of Copelands Ltd. in Stoke-on-Trent is preserved a bottle oven which dates back to A.D. 1800 and which was in use up to 1963. A photograph of this is given in Fig. 15 and this shows the characteristic bottle shape quite clearly.

In the nineteenth century downdraught versions of the bottle kiln were produced. In these kilns the heat from the firemouths generally passed vertically upwards to the crown of the kiln and was then drawn downwards, passing through holes in the floor of the kiln connected to a flue or flues. These either led to a separate chimney or were continued up through the brickwork of the kiln and out through the hole at the top. Several kilns of this type are still in use today.

The downdraught principle is now used extensively in the firing of the intermittent solid-fueled kilns commonly used by many tile- and brick-making companies—particularly where a reduction atmosphere is required.

ADVENT OF THE "TUNNEL" KILN

The advance of science and engineering has been welcomed in the field of pottery firing and the new kiln designs brought about have revolutionized the ceramic industry, enabling it to produce its ware more efficiently and economically and with greater consistency. The introduction of the tunnel kiln was a great step forward. Up to this time pottery had always been fired in intermittent kilns which had ware placed in them when they were cold, after which the kiln was fired and then allowed

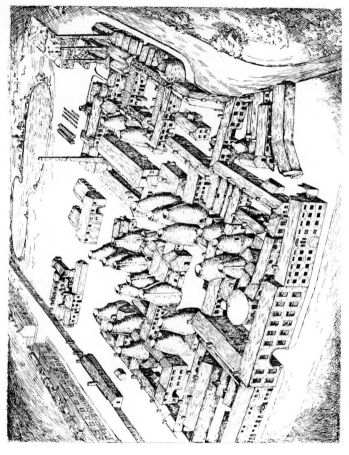

Fig. 14. An illustration of the "Spode" factory of Copelands Ltd. in 1820

(*By courtesy of Messrs. Copeland Ltd.*)

to cool down, so that the ware could then be removed. This inevitably meant that large amounts of heat had to be put into the kiln to heat up the kiln and its contents and after firing one had to wait for the kiln to cool again before the ware could be taken out. The amount of money spent on fuel to heat up the

Fig. 15. Bottle oven built at the Copeland factory about 1800
(*By courtesy of Messrs. Copeland Ltd.*)

structure of the kiln was therefore wasted and in addition production was delayed by the fact that the ware could not be taken from the kiln until this had cooled to a sufficiently low temperature to enable its contents to be handled.

The name "tunnel kiln" describes this type of kiln perfectly.

Fig. 16. Modern intermittent kiln used for reduction firing of tiles and bricks

(By courtesy of Metallic Tile Co.)

Fig. 17. Truck tunnel kiln

(By courtesy of Gibbons Bros. Ltd., Brierley Hill)

Fig. 18. Illuminated internal view of truck tunnel kiln structure
(*By courtesy of The Carborundum Co. Ltd., Trafford Park, Manchester*)

Fig. 19. Placing a truck of ware into a tunnel kiln
(*By courtesy of Gibbons Bros. Ltd., Brierley Hill*)

The ware is carried through a tunnel on a suitable carrier, which may be a truck covered with a refractory lining, a moving refractory belt, or possibly a heat-resisting metal conveyor if the maximum temperature is below 1100°C. In the tunnel the temperature distribution is such that the kiln is at a comparatively low temperature at the entrance, the temperature building up gradually to a maximum more or less in the centre of the kiln and then progressively dropping until a comparatively low point is reached (50–200°C) at the kiln exit.

In most cases a "counterflow system" is operated. With this system the products of combustion generated by the burning of the fuel mainly in the firing zone are drawn towards the entrance end of the kiln, giving up heat to the ware travelling towards the firing zone. As the ware passes from the firing zone into the cooling section of the kiln it is cooled by a stream of air fed in from a fan usually mounted above the kiln exit. This preheated air (referred to as secondary air) is then usually used in fuel combustion and is of considerable importance in this respect as it can result in savings of up to 10–15 per cent on fuel. In the counterflow system the ware fed into the kiln is therefore preheated by exhaust air, and preheated air obtained by passing cool air over the hot trucks leaving the firing zone is used in fuel combustion.

The basic counterflow system, however, has seen many variations and refinements—so much so that many latter-day tunnel kilns are marvels of ingenuity by comparison. It is now quite usual for surplus secondary air to be drawn away from the kiln and fed through ducts to ware-driers used in the clay-ware-making departments. Kilns are often built into virtually two tunnels in the cooling sector: the tunnel through which the ware passes and an outer tunnel or jacket around this through which air is circulated. The brickwork of the inner tunnel (often honeycombed to give greater surface area and thus greater heat pick-up) is heated by the heat radiated from the hot ware and the hot brickwork and transfers its heat by radiation and conduction to the cool air introduced into the outer tunnel which becomes quite hot. This hot air is then piped away to be used as a sort of warm-air central heating for other departments of the factory or is used for ware-drying purposes. Recuperators are also often fitted to tunnel kilns to provide an alternative source of clean hot air. These are usually box-like structures which contain a number of pipes through which clean air is pumped and around which hot air, usually exhaust gas, is passed so that it releases heat to the pipes and thus to the air circulating through them. The modern tunnel kiln may be either gas, oil, or electrically fired; muffle or open flame; large or small; straight or curved.

It should be understood that tunnel kilns utilizing trucks to carry the ware do not fire only one truck at a time. The tunnel kiln itself is filled with a continuous column of trucks which is pushed down the tunnel by the action of a slowly moving ram. The ram itself pushes the column one truck-length down the kiln and then automatically retracts. The exit doors are opened, a truck full of fired ware is pulled out of the kiln, and the exit doors are closed again. The entrance doors are then opened and a further kiln truck full of unfired ware is pushed into position between the ram and the previously introduced truck. The entrance doors are then closed and the ram-pusher started into operation.

The speed of the ram-pusher can be varied very considerably so that the output of the kiln can be regulated to conform to the rate at which ware for firing is produced. In practice, however, every attempt is made to keep tunnel kilns at a constant operating speed for the longest possible time.

Once a tunnel kiln has been heated to its desired temperature it can be kept at this point by comparatively small additions of fuel, and this of course is one of the tunnel kiln's big advantages over its predecessor, the bottle oven, where in every firing as much as 30–40 per cent of the heat generated was used in heating up the kiln brickwork and structure generally. For obvious reasons therefore tunnel kilns are kept in constant operation for the longest possible time—particularly the bigger kilns where just cooling down may take several days and the amount of heat wasted is therefore considerable. When I joined Armitage Ware in 1963 a 300-foot-long tunnel kiln was shut down for overhaul after thirteen years' continuous operation, although at many factories kilns are shut down regularly once a year for inspection and overhaul.

The number of burners fitted and the total length of a tunnel kiln can also vary very widely. Some kilns—particularly those for comparatively low temperatures—may be very small, only 15–20 feet in length, and may have only one burner on each side. On the other hand the biscuit tunnel kiln used by Alfred Meakin Ltd. has over three hundred burners fitted, the kiln being 431 feet long—and longer ones than this are in use.

Perhaps the first tunnel kiln to be constructed was one for firing enamelled ware which was built at Vincennes in France in 1751 and which was in operation until 1802. In 1809, again in France, another kiln was erected for firing decorated earthenware. The ware was placed in iron cages which were pulled through the kiln by a chain. In the late nineteenth century the first tunnel kiln for firing bricks was built by a Swede named Bock. He used rails, trucks, and a sand seal to prevent the heat built up around the ware from leaking downwards past the sides of the trucks and thus overheating the wheel bearings. The kiln was coal-fired, the fuel being fed in at the top of the kiln. In addition to this, hot air was pumped away from the firing zone of the kiln and fed back into the kiln at the entrance to complete the drying of the clay bricks. Tunnel kilns were built for brick factories in America in the early 1890s and in Europe a number of kilns were installed by Dinz between 1900 and 1910, but the first commercially successful type of tunnel kiln was probably the producer-gas-fired one developed about 1910 by Faugeron, a Frenchman. At about this time Conrad Dressler (whose firm was taken over by Gibbons Bros. in 1927) began designing tunnel kilns in Britain on a muffle principle and in 1926 he introduced the multiburner type of kiln, many examples of which are still in economical operation today. There are now many different tunnel kiln manufacturers and consequently many different types of tunnel kiln on the market but the trend is increasingly towards muffle types for the gas- and oil-fired versions, the consequence being a reduction in the use of saggars, and the tunnel kilns are now of comparatively small cross-sectional area so that rapid firing schedules can be obtained yet with an even temperature distribution.

There is also a trend towards smaller continuous kilns, as is typified by the new "Trent" gas-fired kiln. This has refractory bats acting like the truck in a truck tunnel kiln, each bat supporting one or two pots. The comparatively small roller conveyor kiln is also becoming increasingly popular and one of these is illustrated in Fig. 20.

It should not, however, be concluded that the intermittent type of industrial kiln has been completely superseded by the tunnel kiln, for this is certainly not the case. Tunnel kilns lend themselves well to flowline production methods but they are generally large and cost a lot of money to install; consequently they may be unsuitable or too expensive for the smaller company. Many intermittent kilns of the top-hat type are now in successful operation for example.

A top-hat kiln is usually electrically fired, the kiln looking rather like a large box open at its base. The ware to be fired is placed in a refractory base, which usually has shelves built on it so that a large number of pieces can be placed in position. The kiln is then lifted up by crane, gantry, or pneumatically, and lowered over the base which has been tightly packed with pots. After firing, instead of allowing the kiln to cool completely it is lifted up and moved a few yards away where it is lowered into position over another assembly of pots which had been prepared while the previous firing was being carried out. The heat retained by the structure of the kiln after firing is therefore not completely wasted but is utilized in the following firing operation.

Intermittently operated truck kilns are also in use quite extensively. A photograph of one of these appears in Fig. 22, and this is more or less self-explanatory. A truck full of ware is pushed into position inside the kiln and the doors closed. After firing, the truck of ware is removed and immediately replaced by a further truck. The doors are closed and firing recommenced.

"AALI"

The progression from primitive vertical kilns to modern tunnel kilns has not taken place in all countries but only in those areas of the world associated with a reasonable standard of living, such as is generally enjoyed in Europe, Scandinavia, America,

Fig. 20. Gas-fired roller hearth kiln at A. Meakin Ltd.
(By courtesy of Gibbons Bros. Ltd., Brierley Hill)

Australasia, etc. In many parts of the world firing of pottery is still carried out in primitive types of kiln and some of these can be seen in many parts of the middle and far east.

In Bahrain in the Persian Gulf for example, firing is today being carried out in kilns which have been converted from local burial tombs. The village of Aali in Bahrain contains many examples and here the village community produces some excellent wheel-thrown pottery—particularly jugs and pitchers, which are then biscuit-fired using palm fronds as the fuel. The potters, incidentally, make use of their pottery in the biscuit-fired state. Biscuit-fired urns for example are used as water-containers and, as the water, very slowly seeping through the urn, vaporizes on reaching the outside of the vessel, the latent heat required for water vaporization causes the pot and its water content to stay quite cool. This is often a considerable surprise to European visitors who expect the water to be at room temperature—which in the tropics may well be up to 120°F or higher. The villagers know nothing of glazing or glazing processes, although attempts are now being made (1968) to introduce glazing and semi-industrial kilns to convert what is at the moment a dying village craft into a thriving village industry and thus to increase the standard of living of the local community.

Aali contains many burial tombs which could be converted into pottery kilns. To convert them the tombs are dug out more or less into two separate chambers one above the other. The clay pots are placed in the upper chamber, which is some 7 feet in diameter, and the bottom chamber, some 9 feet in diameter, serves as the firemouth, the two chambers being connected by a hole of about 22 inches diameter. The kilns so formed are therefore similar to the simple updraught types used by the Romans, for example, except that the Aali potters also build about four exhaust passages of about 9 inches dia-meter on the outside of the upper chamber and use a lid to seal off the exhaust hole (of about 22 inches diameter) of the upper chamber when necessary. This enables the fires to be kept roaring and provides a better temperature distribution. Firing is by means of palm fronds which are inserted into the firemouth through a hole of some 15 inches diameter.

Fig. 21A. Top hat kiln in raised position

Fig. 21B. Top hat kiln in lowered position
(*By courtesy of Podmore & Sons Ltd.*)

DEVELOPMENT OF THE MODERN STUDIO KILN

Some fifteen to twenty years ago the kilns made for the craft pottery market were scaled-down versions of small industrial kilns, or kilns designed for use in laboratories, pilot plants, etc. They were often intended for use with sophisticated instrumentation and indeed this was sometimes fitted as standard equipment. The handbooks that went with the kilns also were complex and were designed for the eyes of the industrial technician or engineer, and consequently were written in a language

Fig. 22. Intermittent truck kiln
(*By courtesy of Kilns & Furnaces Ltd.*)

that was beyond the comprehension of the craft potter. They were also very expensive and it was only when it became obvious that there was a rapidly increasing demand for smaller and simpler kilns that serious thought was given to producing kilns specifically for the craft potters—kilns that were built to a much simpler and therefore cheaper specification.

The first people to be really aware of the rapidly increasing demands of this sector of the public were, of course, those manufacturers who were already engaged in supplying all the other items of pottery equipment and materials used by the studio potter. These companies were therefore the first to extend their range of activities to kiln building, and the kilns offered were built to a price which was only about one-third of the price of kilns built by the larger manufacturers and designed for use in industry.

Most of the craft pottery material suppliers can now offer a range of kilns from the very smallest size of about 6 inches × 4

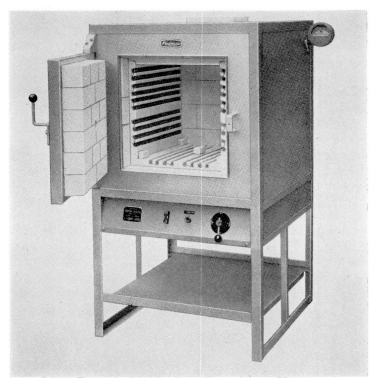

Fig. 23. Typical craft pottery kiln

inches internally, right up to the very much larger kilns now being used by the smaller industrial concerns. The range of kilns available is now quite adequate for the demands of every potter, whether his pottery activities are merely a hobby or whether pottery production is his livelihood.

2 Kiln Construction and Design

The design and construction of studio pottery kilns has entailed a great deal of careful planning. Perfection can seldom be achieved without simplicity but this apparent simplicity of the craft pottery kiln is very misleading. The basic structure of each kiln—particularly of those offered by reputable suppliers —is generally carefully designed to give adequate strength to withstand movement and knocks without being clumsy and excessively heavy. The type of refractory insulation brickwork used in kiln construction is carefully selected and may vary from one size of kiln to another, depending upon the type and thickness of brickwork necessary to reduce heat losses to acceptable limits. The position and optimum size of vent holes, etc., is determined only after careful research and calculation, in order that the firing performance remains quite satisfactory. The bricks themselves have to be well fitted together if the kiln is to give long service, and carefully shaped around the door if the door is to give a snug fit so as to prevent excessive heat losses. Element design and layout is likewise very much a part of the technology of kiln construction if optimum results are to be obtained. A very great deal of thought, calculation and research, as well as a considerable amount of trial and error, have gone into the construction of the modern efficient craft pottery kiln and it is this careful attention to detail that has produced kilns that provide efficiency and long life with freedom from continual maintenance.

In kiln construction the framework is built first and then the brickwork is built within the frame, the electrical fitments and elements being added afterwards.

FRAMEWORK

This is normally built of angle-section steel, although in smaller kilns the framework may be made from strip steel. Angle-section steel is, however, particularly useful as a basis for building in the brickwork as this section gives support on two sides. All joints are normally welded together but the sheet panelling can be fixed with screws or bolts. A photograph of a typical framework assembly is given in Fig. 24.

Fig. 24. Typical steel cabinet used as base structure for craft pottery kiln
(*By courtesy of Kilns & Furnaces Ltd.*)

BRICKWORK

The two types of bricks used generally for the construction of kilns are refractory bricks and refractory insulation bricks and they should not be confused. Refractory bricks are normally fairly dense bricks and are, therefore, comparatively heavy in weight, some of them being heavier than the common house-brick. We have all seen the fireclay brickwork used at the backs of fireplaces: this is a refractory brickwork. Refractory bricks absorb heat comparatively quickly and if one face of the brick is exposed to heat the other side of the brick will quickly become warm as the heat is conducted through the brick. Refractory bricks, therefore, tend to be used in those positions where heat

Fig. 25. Completed kiln
(*By courtesy of Kilns & Furnaces Ltd.*)

loss is not quite so important—for example, for the building of chimneys or for the exterior brickwork of kilns. This type of brick is seldom used in the manufacture of electric kilns, for although they are quite capable of withstanding the heat generated inside the kiln this heat would very easily be conducted away if the bricks were used for the interior lining of the kiln and the use of these bricks would, of course, considerably increase the weight of the kiln. This would make carriage charges, etc., more expensive and movement of the kilns generally more difficult. The bricks used for the manufacture of electric kilns are normally of the refractory insulation type. These have all the heat-resisting qualities of refractory bricks but are very porous indeed. Air, as we all know, is a good insulator and the huge number of air pockets inside these bricks makes the bricks good insulators of heat so that if one face of the brick is exposed to heat it takes a considerable time before this heat is transmitted through the brick to the opposite face. This pore structure makes the bricks very light in weight, so much so that one often sees workmen in kiln manufacturing workshops carrying a huge stack of bricks quite unaided. This can be quite an awe-inspiring sight for one is accustomed to estimating the weight of a brick by thinking in terms of common house-bricks, and probably about ten or a dozen of these are the maximum that a person can carry fairly easily. However, whereas an ordinary house-brick weighs about 8 pounds, a typical refractory insulation brick would weigh about $2\frac{1}{2}$ pounds for a brick of the same size.

The very high porosity (i.e. pore structure) gives another very useful property to these bricks; i.e. it makes them comparatively soft and easy to cut with a normal hacksaw. These bricks can therefore be very easily shaped so that cutting a groove in them to take elements, or boring holes in them, presents no problem.

The brickwork is built into the framework using a heat-resisting compound of a similar composition to the bricks themselves. Care is taken to make the joints as fine as possible as large gaps between bricks filled with jointing compound are unsightly in appearance and a possible source of weakness.

ELECTRICAL WIRING AND FITMENTS

With most designs of kilns the "works" such as junction boxes, terminals, etc., are fitted at the back of the kiln and access to them can normally be gained by removing a panel from the kiln. Electrical kilns, of course, take quite a considerable current—especially the larger sizes—and when the kilns are switched on and off the switching device must be robust to withstand the sparking which may occur. The switching is therefore often done through a contactor, which is merely a robust relay enabling the kiln to be switched on and off without burning away any of the connexions, etc. Smaller kilns may not be fitted with a contactor and this is why one is normally required if any form of energy regulator is subsequently fitted to the kiln, for these energy regulators operate by continually switching the kiln on and off.

Electricity supply to each element is normally made through

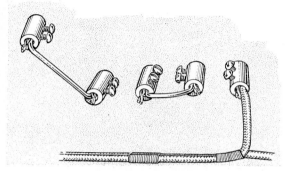

Fig. 26. Brass connectors used for element connexion

a small brass connector. Steel connectors tend to oxidize too readily.

Some kilns are fitted as standard with an energy regulator complete with a little pilot light which is switched automatically on and off as the energy regulator switches the current to the elements on and off. A few kilns are fitted with a door switch as a standard item—particularly where the kiln is to be used for metal enamelling. The majority of kilns used by the craft and school potter are, however, merely fitted with a rotary switch which normally has four settings marked upon it, denoted "Off," "Low," "Medium," and "High." These settings refer to the amount of current which is allowed to flow to the elements and thus the rate at which the kiln increases its temperature.

Usually the kiln is fitted with a control panel—rather like the dashboard of a motor car—on which the electrical accessories mentioned above are fitted. Some kilns, however, are supplied with a separate control panel which has to be mounted on an adjacent wall or other convenient surface.

Most kiln manufacturers build the door-closing device in such a way that a padlock can be fitted so that the kiln door cannot be opened unless the padlock is removed.

ELEMENTS

There are several types of elements which can be fitted to kilns, but the most popular types are those known as Kanthal A and Kanthal A1 elements. Other types of elements, such as Nichrome, Super Kanthal or silicon carbide, can also be fitted. Let us now look at each of these element types in turn.

Nichrome elements

These, as the name implies, are made basically from an alloy of nickel and chromium and are fitted to kilns which are not required to operate at temperatures above about 1050°C. The fitting of these elements may enable a kiln to attain temperatures up to 1150°C but at temperatures as high as this the elements would very quickly burn away and so for all practical purposes the maximum temperature is normally kept down to 1000°C or thereabouts. This temperature, however, is quite sufficient for enamelling or for majolica and low-temperature glazes. Nichrome wire is comparatively cheap and is, incidentally, the wire used for domestic electric fires. One cannot, however, use the wire from a domestic fire in one of these kilns for within the enclosed kiln such wire would very quickly burn away. A free flow of air around electric-fire elements helps to keep the actual element temperature within reasonable limits. This would not happen inside a kiln.

Kanthal A and A1 elements

These are made from alloys of iron, aluminium, chromium and cobalt and it is claimed that these alloys will give three times the life of the Nichrome types at similar temperatures. These alloys do not contain nickel and the great disadvantage is that once they have been fired they become very brittle and have to be well supported in the kiln. Any knocks or shaking can easily break them at this stage. Kanthal A elements will allow the kiln to reach maximum temperatures of about 1200°C but Kanthal A1 elements will allow a maximum operating temperature of 1300°C. These are the two types of element most commonly used in electric kilns. An important feature of Kanthal wire is that after firing, the wire becomes coated with aluminium oxide, which protects the wire from attack by most of the harmful gases. Exposure to reducing atmospheres will, however, very quickly remove this coating and the elements will then deteriorate very quickly unless the coating is restored by an oxidizing fire. Alkali vapours and halogen vapours—for example, fluorine, iodine, etc.—are harmful to elements and so is lead vapour. Kanthal wire is not attacked, however, by sulphur compounds as is Nichrome wire.

Super Kanthal and silicon carbide elements
These are used only for very high-temperature work beyond the temperatures used in pottery production. Temperatures of 1600°C can be attained with Super Kanthal and 1500°C with silicon carbide. Both types of elements are very expensive and as the resistance of the silicon carbide elements increases with each firing, voltage regulators have to be fitted. Both types are normally used only for industrial applications.

Elements of the Nichrome and Kanthal types are wound into a continuous spiral which is usually formed into a hairpin shape, i.e. two rows of element coils joined at one end. The last six to nine inches of each end of the element is not coiled but is left as a straight wire so that these element "tails," as they are called, can be pushed through holes drilled through the rear wall of the kiln and connected to brass connectors in the connexion chamber at the rear of the kiln.

The determination of the correct amount of element wire to use for the elements is part of the science of kiln technology and is thus one of the more difficult problems which face the "do-it-yourself" enthusiast. Not only does the kiln technologist calculate how much wire of a certain grade is needed to supply the necessary amount of heat for a given kiln size, he also has to adjust his data to conform to different voltages and he has to calculate the number of coils into which the elements must be made—which must be within certain limits if optimum element life is to be obtained.

Most high-temperature kilns are designed to give a very even temperature distribution at around 1100°C. At temperatures above and below this point there tends to be an increasing degree of temperature variation. In an attempt to obtain the least possible variation over a wide range of temperature some kiln manufacturers fit graded elements into their kilns. This does have the slight disadvantage that it is not possible to keep one spare element to guard against a risk of element failure since one does not know which element will fail first, but this disadvantage is more than compensated by the more even firing characteristics.

An alternative way to obtain an even temperature distribution over the complete firing cycle is to wire the elements into groups or "banks" and to fit an independent energy regulator to control each bank of elements. Two or three thermocouples are then fitted to the kiln, so that if the temperature in one part of the kiln shows signs of lagging behind the rest of the kiln the energy regulator controlling the elements in that region can be turned to a higher setting so that more heat is introduced. This system is often used with large studio and semi-industrial kilns but is not usual with the kilns more commonly used by craft and school potters because of the expense involved.

The vast majority of craft pottery kilns are of the exposed element type. This means that the elements are supported in grooves or channels cut into the walls of the kiln leaving the elements clearly visible. This method is much cheaper, more efficient, and lends itself to easier maintenance than the alternative muffle type of kiln in which the elements are completely hidden from sight behind a thin wall of refractory material made of sillimanite or, better still, of silicon carbide (Carborundum), through which the heat has to pass to reach the ware.

If ever it is necessary to replace a burnt-out element always quote the serial number of your kiln to the kiln manufacturer, indicating which particular element has failed and always make certain that *every* trace of the burnt-out element has been removed from the element grooves before fitting the replacement. This is most important.

THE FIRST FIRING

Before any kiln is put into use, it should be fired slowly to a temperature no higher than 100 or 200 degrees below the maximum firing temperature for which it was designed. This gentle firing drives away any moisture present in the brickwork, after which the kiln is ready to be put into full service.

After this first firing has taken place, it may be noticed that a few fine cracks have formed in the interior brickwork of the kiln. These cracks will close up when the kiln is next heated and open up again when the kiln is subsequently cooled. They therefore serve as expansion joints and are in no way detrimental to the operation of the kiln.

3 Kiln Accessories and Instrumentation

There are many different types of "extras" which can be fitted to pottery kilns, some of which are standard fitments of certain models produced by some manufacturers. The more popular ones are detailed below.

THE ROTARY SWITCH

Some provision for varying the rate of temperature increase of a pottery kiln is more or less essential. The rotary switch, otherwise known as a three-position or four-position switch, is the simplest way of providing this service, and most craft pottery kilns are therefore fitted with one of these by the manufacturer.

The switch itself has four positions only at which it can be set. These positions are generally indicated by the words "Off," "Low," "Medium" and "High." These settings refer to the rate at which the kiln will increase its temperature.

The switch is usually wired in what is referred to as a "series/parallel" circuit, which is an electrical way of varying the manner in which the elements are wired into the mains supply at each position of the switch. This effectively changes the amount of heat generated by the elements at each setting.

As the electricity supply is not switched on and off to retard the temperature rise, as is done with an energy regulator, a contactor is not required.

With most kilns the operation is such that when the switch is set at its "low" setting the energized elements do not actually glow, as does an electric fire, but remain at "black heat."

The rotary switch unit costs approximately £4.

ENERGY REGULATOR

This is purely a retarding medium for controlling the rate of temperature increase, which it does by controlling the heat input to the kiln. It comprises an automatic switching device, the time periods during which the switch contacts are open and closed being infinitely variable. The length of time during which the contacts are closed is controlled by an adjusting knob which is usually calibrated from 0 to 100 per cent. When the knob is set to its 100 per cent setting the contacts are closed all the time and so the electricity supply to the elements is

Fig. 27. Front control panel of kiln showing door switch and energy regulator

never interrupted, the kiln therefore heating up at its maximum rate.

The energy regulator is mounted either on the kiln or on a separate control panel unit which can be mounted adjacent to the kiln. A small indicator light is often incorporated in the regulator which is switched on when the regulator switch contacts are closed and switches off again when the contacts open. When the kiln elements are receiving electricity supply the indicator light therefore lights up and switches off again when the element supply is cut off.

An energy regulator is a very useful piece of equipment as the rate of temperature increase can be controlled so easily. Thus if thick-walled pots are being fired the rate of temperature increase can very easily be reduced. If a pyrometer is fitted to the kiln and one wished to maintain the kiln at a particular temperature the energy regulator setting could be adjusted until a position was found at which the elements were switched on and off at a rate slow enough to prevent any further temperature rise but fast enough to prevent the temperature from dropping. This procedure, however, should only be done for short periods as otherwise the temperature may begin to drift.

The price of an energy regulator varies from about £3 10s. to £30, depending upon what accessories are already fitted to the kiln (particularly a contactor) and the size of the kiln. An energy regulator and contactor is a standard fitting on some kilns such as Podmore P.7, P.8 and P.9 but is an optional extra, for example, for their P.4, P.5 and P.6 models.

There is a type of energy regulator known as a Simmerstat which is often fitted to kilns. However, the lowest setting of a Simmerstat control allows an appreciably faster rate of temperature increase than one would obtain from the lowest setting of the standard (Sunvic) form of energy regulator, the Sunvic type of energy regulator giving a wider range of control.

DOOR SWITCH

This is a device which is designed to isolate the electrical supplies to the kiln elements when the kiln door is open. The usual type of switch consists of a metal bracket which is fixed to the lower edge of the kiln door and which depresses a plunger fitted to the front or underside of the kiln; this in turn operates the contactor relay, thus allowing current to flow to the kiln elements. When the door is opened the plunger is released, which switches the contactor relay to its off position, thus cutting off the electricity supply to the elements. Prices vary from about £4 for the door switch, plus the price of a mains contactor if this is not already a standard fitment on the kiln.

Door switches are often fitted to the kilns used in schools and many teachers regard them as an essential item. With most kilns the elements do not begin to glow for an appreciable number of seconds after the kiln has been switched on even if the kiln energy regulator is set at its highest setting, and if a rotary switch only is fitted and this is set at its low position the elements may never glow but remain at black heat. Under these conditions the risk of electrocution arising from a child's opening the kiln door and placing his hands on the elements must not be overlooked. Door switches are also an additional safety precaution if one is working on the kiln—perhaps replacing elements—and someone switches on!

CASTEL LOCK

This is a cylinder locking switch and serves a similar purpose to the door switch mentioned above. A key is, of course, supplied with the switch and the kiln will not operate until the key is inserted and turned in a clockwise direction. If the key is removed at any time the electrical supply to the elements is broken and the kiln is therefore rendered "safe" if the door is opened. Cylinder locking switches cost from about £5 upwards and have to be used in conjunction with a contactor, as with the type of door switch mentioned above.

HEAT FUSE

This is a fusible link which is fitted into a kiln in a similar manner to a thermocouple, i.e. with a part of it projecting into the kiln firing chamber. Heat fuses are manufactured to conform to a wide range of individual temperatures and when this

Fig. 28. Heat fuse

temperature is reached the heat fuse melts, thus breaking a circuit and cutting off the supply to the kiln.

Heat fuses are not used to control the end point of a kiln firing but are used as a safety valve to cut off the power supply when the temperature for some reason reaches a level at which damage is likely to result. Fuses to melt at about 1350°C are often fitted for example to kilns being fired up to 1300°C, as 1350°C is beyond the maximum temperature at which the pottery is fired, but below 1375°C, at which temperature damage to the bricks or shelves is likely to result.

Prices per fuse are from £5 upwards.

TIME SWITCH

There are, of course, many different types of time switch differing in size and complexity.

Those which are sometimes used in kiln circuits, generally cost from £8 upwards. They are fitted with a time scale graduated with twenty-four hourly divisions, each division normally being sub-divided still further into proportions of one hour. Two separate pointers are normally fitted alongside the

Fig. 29. Time switch
Set to switch on at 2.30 p.m. and off again at 2.15 a.m.
(*By courtesy of Sangamo Weston Ltd.*)

scale, the pointers being movable so that they can be set to any desired setting. When the electricity supply is switched on the time switch begins to operate like a clock and will automatically operate a relay to switch on the kiln when the time indicated by one of the two pointers reaches a certain reference point which denotes the actual time of day. The kiln will then be switched off when the second pointer reaches the reference point. In addition to this, certain models can be programmed to operate at the required times on a required day, i.e. they have day control in addition to hour control.

Time switches can be useful under certain circumstances but one must remember that the length of time taken for any firing will vary from one firing to the next depending upon the variation in the amount of ware inside the kiln and in the voltage of the electricity supply for example.

About ten years ago I carried out many firings at RAF Marham, in Norfolk, with a small kiln fitted with a time switch. I found the time switch very useful for automatically switching on the kiln in the early hours of the morning while I was soundly asleep and I then finished off the firing using Staffordshire cones at around midday, which was my most convenient time. I did find that the firing time varied by as much as half-an-hour either way but after a while I could guess approximately how long the firing was likely to take with that particular kiln to within fifteen to twenty minutes. This represented little more than one cone variation and with the types of clay and glazes I was using this would not have had catastrophic effects had I relied solely on the time switch. The time switch, incidentally, was set to switch off about twenty minutes after the time at which I had estimated the firing would near completion so that if for some reason I could not be available to attend the kiln as it reached the required temperature, the time switch would automatically switch off.

THE KILN SITTER

This is an American device marketed in Britain by Bernard W. E. Webber Ltd. and provides a means of arranging the collapse of a miniature Staffordshire cone to operate a switching device to cut off the electrical supply to the kiln.

As will be seen from Fig. 30 the equipment comprises a metal box containing a heavy-duty mechanical switch from which projects a heavy porcelain tube on the end of which is carried the miniature cone. A high-temperature heat-resistant feeler rod lies on the cone and a claw fitted to the feeler rod holds a counterweight in position.

The equipment is set to commence firing by pressing in a self-locking push-button to close the switch. When the required temperature has been reached the cone bends, thus altering the setting of the feeler rod, which results in the claw

Fig. 30. The kiln sitter
(*By courtesy of Webbers Ltd.*)

being lifted thus releasing the weight. In falling this weight releases with a snap action the heavy-duty switch.

Full instructions are provided and the equipment is easily fitted by drilling a 1-inch hole through the kiln case and brick-work, inserting the ceramic tube and drilling and screwing the metal case to the kiln case with the screws provided. The price is similar to or slightly less than that of an indicating pyrometer.

4 Pyroscopes and Temperature Control

Some means of controlling the firing of a kiln is essential to obtain consistently good pottery. Before the intensive study of pyrometric practice the sense organs were the only means of determining temperatures and kiln firemen estimated the temperature of a kiln by reference to the degree and colour of the glow inside it. The determination of temperature by sight and feel, however, can only be an approximation and it is quite inadequate for modern industrial practices and the modern studio potter.

PYROMETERS AND PYROSCOPES

There are basically two methods of controlling a kiln firing: by the use of pyrometers and by the use of pyroscopes (pyroscopes such as Staffordshire cones are often referred to as pyrometric cones). Pyrometers and Pyroscopes are, however, often used in conjunction as they measure two completely different functions. Pyrometers measure temperature, pyroscopes measure heat work.

Pyroscopes are indicators made of ceramic mixtures based on silicates. The chemical nature of silicate mixtures is such that they do not have definite melting points but they have a temperature range in which part of the mixture is melted and the remainder is solid. In this temperature range the process of glass formation (vitrification) takes place. When a sufficient degree of vitrification occurs the pyroscope can no longer support itself and bends or collapses, thus giving a visible indication. There are, however, two ways of attaining this result. The first is to heat the pyroscope to a temperature high enough to produce this effect quickly. The second is to heat to a slightly lower temperature but to hold this temperature for a longer time.

Since pyroscopes tend to be of a similar composition to

pottery bodies they offer a very good means of controlling the finishing point of a kiln firing. Pottery is correctly fired when the correct degree of vitrification has taken place—as are pyroscopes. If a kiln firing is done slowly this will be reached at a lower temperature than when the firing is done very quickly. Thus the reliance on pyrometers alone to determine the finishing point of a kiln firing can be a little misleading.

STAFFORDSHIRE CONES

These offer possibly the most important and useful way of controlling a kiln firing for the studio potter. They are commonly classified as pyroscopes; Bullers rings and Holdcroft bars fall into the same category.

Suppliers generally offer Staffordshire cones in two sizes— "Standard" cones which are $2\frac{1}{2}$ inches tall and "Miniature" cones which are 1 inch tall. The cones themselves are of a three-sided conical shape. They are made of carefully controlled mixtures of ceramic materials, which mixtures are so designed as to give a graduated scale of fusing temperatures at approximately 20-degree intervals.

The cones which melt at the lower temperatures contain a higher proportion of fluxes than those melting at the higher

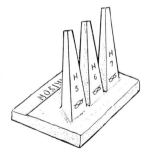

Fig. 31.
Cones correctly set

Fig. 32.
Cones correctly fired (to H6)

temperatures, which contain increasingly larger proportions of refractory oxides. This melting or fusing temperature is denoted by a number which is stamped into the back of the cone and by reference to the Staffordshire cone chart one can obtain an approximate melting-point for each of the different numbers. It is, however, commonly assumed that Staffordshire cones will always melt at the temperature indicated in this chart. This is not so. Staffordshire cones melt and collapse not necessarily when a specific temperature has been attained but also when they have been subjected to a certain temperature, or rate of temperature increase, for a certain length of time. It is this time factor which is so important: if one fired a kiln, say, to 1000°C in, say, three to four hours, the pottery ware fired in the kiln would not be fired to the same degree as ware fired to 1000°C over a period of eight to ten hours. This, of course, is rather obvious but many potters erroneously believe that because the ware has been fired to its recommended temperature the pottery is bound to be fired correctly. If, in the two cases listed above, the fire was being controlled solely by means of a pyrometer then the kiln would have been switched off in both cases when the temperature reached 1000°C and the ware fired in three to four hours would not have been properly fired and, indeed, would probably be underfired when withdrawn from the kiln. This is where the time factor of Staffordshire cones is so useful. As I have mentioned, Staffordshire cones only collapse when subjected to heat for a certain length of time and if they are fired too rapidly they will not collapse until a temperature is reached which may be considerably above that indicated by the number stamped on the back of them. Similarly, if the cones are fired too slowly then they will probably collapse at a temperature earlier than that indicated by the cone number. In this way Staffordshire cones give an indication of the amount of heat work applied to the ware and not merely the temperature to which the ware is subjected. Pyrometers measure temperature; pyroscopes measure heat work. The two are not the same.

It should be noted that other factors can influence the temperature at which Staffordshire cones collapse. If they are used in a strongly reducing atmosphere then it is possible for a chemical reaction to take place which results in a hard refractory skin being formed on the outside of the cone. The cone may then stand quite upright and the temperature of the kiln continue to increase considerably beyond the point at which the cone was supposed to have collapsed. It is even possible for this hard skin to be formed and yet for the inside of the cone to melt and run away, with the result that the refractory shell of the cone which may be still standing upright misleads the operator. Sulphur gases can also attack Staffordshire cones, resulting in bloating and a grey discoloration which, again, tends to distort the collapsing temperature.

One of the most important considerations in the use of pyrometric cones is the way in which they are mounted. This is generally done by inserting the base of the cones either into special cone holders or into a pad of plastic clay, but regardless of the type of mounting it is important that all the cones be embedded to the same depth. It is necessary for the cones to be placed at an angle of about 15° to the vertical and to ensure this the manufacturer slants the base of the cone so that this inclination is automatically brought about when the cone is stood upright.

It is usual to use a series of three cones for each firing, one cone indicating a temperature about 20 degrees below the temperature to which the ware is to be fired, one cone indicating the required temperature, and one cone indicating a temperature some 20 degrees above the required one. In this way the collapse of the lower cone serves as a warning that the temperature is rising to the point at which the second cone will collapse (at which time the kiln should, of course, be switched off). The third cone serves as a guard—as an indication that the ware has not been overfired. An alternative layout sometimes used by the craft potter is to dispense with the "guard" cone and to use an extra warning cone collapsing at a temperature some 40 degrees below the required temperature of the fire.

It is important to place the cones in some definite order and this is generally done by placing the cones from left to right in order of increasing fusion point so that the cone on the extreme right will be the last to go down. The correct firing of any cone will be indicated when the cone bends over so that its tip bends down and touches the base on which the cone is mounted. This is referred to as the end-point of the cone. If the temperature continues to increase the cone will, of course, collapse still further and eventually melt completely.

Unfortunately the cone manufacturers have not, until recently, standardized their products. However, in 1964 a "British Standard" was set (B.S. 1041: Part 7: 1964) and the British Ceramic Research Association recommended the adoption of those cones which have an "H" prefix to the cone number as these were made to conform to the British Standard. Staffordshire cones which do not bear this "H" prefix (i.e. are stamped "01" instead of "H01," for example) are the "old" series of cones, production of which has now ceased although some suppliers still have limited stocks. It is certainly true to say that although the "old" series and "H" series cones give reasonably similar indications over a certain range of temperature, some of the old series of cones can be as much as 30 to 40°C different in collapsing temperature to the equivalent "H" series cone. It is becoming increasingly difficult to obtain the old series of Staffordshire cones but if by any chance you do have a stock of these and have controlled your kiln firings with them do not under any circumstances switch over to "H" series cones until you have carried out simple comparison tests.

BULLERS RINGS

These are another form of pyroscope made from a carefully controlled mixture of ceramic materials. They take the form of a flat ring some 3 inches in diameter and about $\frac{1}{4}$ inch thick and with a hole in the middle, and are used in conjunction with a Bullers ring gauge.

Bullers rings are placed vertically in a special holder and after firing they will, of course, have contracted considerably with a consequent reduction in diameter. This degree of contraction is measured by placing the ring into the gauge and observing the number indicated on the scale, which is calibrated from zero (zero being the indicated reading of an unfired Bullers ring). The number indicated on the scale is referred to in the Pottery industry as the number of "pips." Potters consequently tend to speak of a Bullers ring firing of a certain number of pips. Bullers rings are not commonly used by studio potters, because of the expense of the gauge and the amount of space taken up by the ring during firing. They are, however, very extensively used by the larger industrial concerns because of the uniform rate of contraction over a wide range of temperature. This enables the tunnel kiln fireman to determine the amount of heat work being put into the kiln at any point along its length by the simple expedient of opening up the appropriate spy-hole (these are situated at intervals all the way along the side walls of the tunnel kiln), inserting a poker and "hooking" the Bullers ring through its centre hole from the car travelling through the kiln immediately opposite the spy-hole. When cool, the ring can be measured in the gauge and, if the reading is substantially different from those previously taken from the same point, corrective action can be taken.

HOLDCROFT BARS

These are another form of pyroscope which take the form of bars of ceramic material of a square cross-section of about $\frac{1}{4}$ to

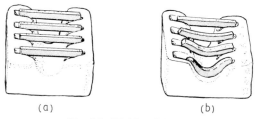

(a)   (b)

Fig. 33. Holdcroft bars
(*a*) Before using.   (*b*) After using.

$\frac{1}{2}$ inch and about 3 inches in length. They are stamped with a number from one to forty, which can be related to a chart graduated from 600° to 1550°C.

Holdcroft bars are placed horizontally on two supports so that the ends of the bars only are supported. The ceramic mixtures of which they are made begin to melt so that the bars collapse in the middle when the approximate firing temperatures, indicated in the charts, have been reached.

5 An Introduction to Thermoelectricity

The basic form of pyrometer is a simple temperature-indicating device consisting of a thermocouple and a galvanometer. There are, of course, special ways of adapting this basic instrument to enable it to control the firing temperature or firing cycle to a considerable degree—and these variations will be discussed more fully in the next chapter.

THERMOCOUPLES

However, before we can go on to discuss the different types of pyrometers which are available to the craft potter we should perhaps discuss thermocouples in greater detail for this is the "working end" of the pyrometer, the end which projects inside the kiln and which generates the current which is measured by the instrument fixed outside the kiln.

If two different metals are drawn into wires and they are joined together at one end, a small electric current is generated when this joint of the two wires is heated. The greater the amount of heat applied to the junction the greater will be the voltage generated in the wires. By measuring this voltage one can, therefore, get some indication of the amount of heat being applied to the junction of the wires. If the junction of the wires is plunged into, say, boiling water, the voltage recorded on the galvanometer (the instrument) can be marked with the temperature 100°C, since this is the boiling-point of water. Similarly, if the end of the thermocouple is plunged into boiling sulphur, the reading on the galvanometer can be calibrated for 444°C, since this is the boiling point of sulphur. In this way we can calibrate our galvanometer to read degrees of temperature as well as voltage, and if this were done over a range of different temperatures we should then have an instrument which would be capable of measuring temperature. We should have created a thermoelectric pyrometer, to give this instrument its full name. We can see that this is made up of a thermocouple and a galvanometer. The voltage generated by thermocouples is, incidentally, very small, being measured in thousandths of a volt (millivolts) rather than in volts.

It should be noted that there are several different types of thermocouples and the amount of voltage generated at any particular temperature differs with each type. For this reason one cannot generally use one galvanometer and attach to this different types of thermocouples. The metals from which the thermocouple wires are made differ with different types of thermocouples. Some of the more commonly used thermocouples are as follows.

Copper–Constantan

Copper for one wire, Constantan (made of 60 per cent of copper and 40 per cent of nickel) for the other. This can be used for temperatures up to 600°F (315°C).

Nichrome–Constantan

Nichrome (an alloy of 90 per cent of nickel and 10 per cent of chromium) for one wire and Constantan for the other. This can be used for temperatures up to 1600°F (870°C).

Iron–Constantan

Iron for one wire and Constantan for the other. Used for temperatures up to 1600°F (870°C).

Chromel–Alumel

Chromel (a nickel-chromium alloy) for one wire, Alumel (an alloy of nickel, aluminium, manganese and silicon) for the other. Used for temperatures up to 2100°F (1150°C).

Platinum–10 per cent rhodium

An alloy of 10 per cent of rhodium, 90 per cent of platinum for one wire and pure platinum for the other. Used for temperatures up to 2700°F (1480°C).

Platinum–13 per cent rhodium

An alloy of 13 per cent rhodium and 87 per cent of platinum for one wire and pure platinum for the other. Used for temperatures up to 2700°F (1480°C).

Of these, the types normally used in ceramics are the Chromel–Alumel and the platinum-rhodium and platinum types. Platinum is, of course, a very expensive metal and for this reason the thermocouples based on platinum are very much more expensive than the Chromel–Alumel types. It will be seen that temperatures up to 1150°C can be satisfactorily recorded by the use of Chromel–Alumel thermocouples and if one is not going to fire to temperatures higher than this then for economic considerations this thermocouple is to be preferred to the platinum type.

The thermocouple wires have to be insulated from one another and this is generally done by passing them through small porcelain tubes. The insulated wires are then immersed in a refractory sheath in the form of a tube closed at one end which serves to protect the thermocouple from certain harmful gases present in the kiln atmosphere. The other end of the sheath terminates in the thermocouple head on which are located the terminals to which the wires carrying the voltage back to the galvanometer are connected.

The voltage generated by the thermoelectric pyrometer is due to two completely different effects known as the Thomson and Peltier effects respectively. Peltier discovered in 1834 that when two different metals are joined together a difference in voltage exists between them and that this varies with the temperature of the junction. Usually when the junction is heated the voltage generated increases proportionally but with certain metals the rate of increase of voltage begins to decrease again at certain temperature ranges. In 1854 Thomson discovered that when a length of metallic wire is heated at one end a difference in voltage between the ends is created. Sometimes the heated end is at a higher voltage than the other but sometimes the reverse is true.

When selecting wires from which to make thermocouples the manufacturers must ensure that the Peltier and Thomson effects complement one another. They must, therefore, choose two wires whose Thomson effects are in opposite directions and vary uniformly with temperature. They must ensure that the voltage generated by the Peltier effect is such that the wire carrying the negative Thomson voltage must be the positive element as far as the Peltier voltage is concerned. The voltages created by the two different effects will then support one another and will tend to vary uniformly with temperature provided that the cold end of the thermo-couple wires is held at a known and constant temperature.

The cold end of the thermocouple is generally referred to as the "cold junction," the end of the thermocouple projecting into the firing chamber being referred to as the "hot junction."

It should always be remembered that the voltage generated by a thermocouple is dependent upon the difference in

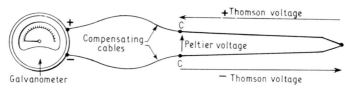

Fig. 34. Simplified sketch of a thermoelectric pyrometer

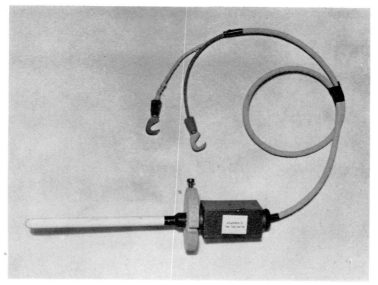

Fig. 35. Typical thermocouple fitted with compensating cables

temperature between the hot and cold junctions and to register temperature accurately it is very important for the cold junction to be kept always at the same known temperature. The reason for this is that the wires which connect the cold junction of the thermocouple to the galvanometer (these wires are referred to as compensating cables) will in themselves generate a small voltage between the cold junction of the thermocouple and the galvanometer. In this case the galvanometer serves to unite the ends of the compensating cables. The Peltier effect of the compensating cables will vary if the temperature of this junction of the cables is allowed to vary. Similarly, any cold junction variation will affect the voltage created still further. Providing that we keep the cold junction and the galvanometer at a constant temperature the small Peltier voltage generated by the compensating cables via the galvanometer can be corrected by calibrating the latter.

If heat is applied to the thermocouple or compensating wires at some point along their length the voltages created by this additional source of heat will tend to cancel themselves out, provided that the respective temperatures of the hot and cold junctions are not affected.

The cold junction

We have mentioned earlier that the cold junction of a thermocouple should always be at a constant and known temperature but since operating errors when using pyrometers are so often due to the cold junction this subject is worthy of further mention.

Let us refer to Fig. 34 showing a typical thermocouple, compensating cable, and galvanometer layout. Let us also assume that this thermocouple is of the Chromel–Alumel type which generates a voltage increasing uniformly with increase in temperature (this is not the case incidentally with platinum–rhodium thermocouples and many other types). We will assume that the hot junction of this thermocouple is at a temperature which results in a reading of 1000°C on the galvanometer. We will further assume that the galvanometer is at a temperature of 20°C but that the connexions between the thermocouple and the compensating cables labelled "C" in the diagram are at 35°C, as a result of being overheated for some reason. In the example just mentioned, the cold junction is at "C" and not at the galvanometer but the temperature of the galvanometer is often taken as being the cold junction temperature.

6 Temperature-measuring Instruments (Pyrometers)

Temperature-measuring instruments are of different types but the ones generally used by studio potters consist of a thermocouple attached by compensating cables to an instrument which transforms the voltages fed into it from the thermocouple into degrees of temperature which are indicated on a scale. The indicating instrument itself is generally one of two types: either a galvanometer (i.e. a millivoltmeter) which is similar in design to the ammeter fitted to many motor-car dashboards, etc., or a potentiometer. The standard pyrometer generally has a simple galvanometer as the recording instrument whereas the more sophisticated recording instruments generally have potentiometric systems or a combination of the two.

POTENTIOMETERS

The word "potentiometric" occurs frequently in temperature measurement systems and describes merely the system used inside the recording instrument to measure accurately and to convert into degrees of temperature the very small voltages fed into it from the thermocouple. A potentiometer compares these minute voltages with a precise voltage generated by a battery system inside the instrument.

The difference between the two is measured and made to operate a pointer which indicates degrees of temperature (*see* Fig. 36). This method gives more accurate measurement and a more robust instrument than the galvanometer usually used for the standard pyrometer, which directly measures the voltage from the thermocouple.

In this chapter I will briefly discuss the different types of instruments commonly used by studio and school potters. Each instrument has a different function although some instruments offer the same means of control as others but in a more sophisticated form. Obviously the choice of the most suitable type of instrumentation will depend not only upon the job it has to do but largely also upon personal preference and to a certain degree upon whether the kiln operator can be constantly available or is available only for short periods to attend the kiln. If one has the time to attend to the kiln whenever necessary to change settings, switch off, etc., then one does not really require more than Staffordshire cones, an energy regulator (or three-position switch), and perhaps also a standard pyrometer.

The cost of certain instruments, such as the Thermolimit, temperature regulator, controlling pyrometer and programme controller, will vary to some extent depending upon what type of electrical components are already fitted to the kiln. Each of these instruments, for example, must be wired in conjunction with a contactor, the price of which increases with kiln size. Contactors are fitted as a standard fitment to some kilns and are fitted on all kilns which use a Sunvic-type energy regulator: they are therefore standard fitments on the Podmore P.7, P.8 and P.9 kilns but not on the P.1 to P.6 kilns. Prices quoted for the control instruments mentioned above generally include the price of the necessary contactor unless it is known that the kiln for which the instrument is required is already fitted with a contactor. Thus the price for a controlling pyrometer will be lower for a P.9 kiln than it would be for a P.1 model.

Most temperature-indicating instruments are of a delicate nature and the manufacturers stipulate that they should be serviced at regular intervals if accuracy and reliability are to be maintained. Furthermore, it is always a wise precaution to carry out the first few firings by relying upon Staffordshire cones and to use the instrument solely as a reference—just to ensure that it is functioning correctly.

Important "Do's" and "Don'ts" when installing pyrometers
Don't connect electric mains supply to pyrometer/thermo-couple terminals.

Don't run the compensating cables near or parallel to electric mains as otherwise the compensating cables will have an electric current induced in them from the mains cables, which will result in inaccurate readings on the instrument.

Don't drill holes in the pyrometer case for any purpose whatsoever. If a different mounting is required the pyrometer should be returned to the factory for modification.

Don't open the pyrometer when dust, dirt, fumes or metal dust are in the atmosphere.

Don't use ordinary copper cable for connecting the thermocouple to the pyrometer, as this will not compensate for temperature changes.

Don't shorten or lengthen the cable or thermocouple as the pyrometer has been calibrated for external resistance.

Other important points

The temperature inside the kiln is indicated on the pyrometer dial at all times. Do not adjust the instrument to read zero if the kiln is at room temperature.

When pyrometers are being packed for despatch, a connecting wire is always joined between the pyrometer terminals. This "shunt" wire prevents the indicator needle from swinging about violently if the pyrometer is jolted, and must be removed before the instrument can be used.

Pyrometers must not be positioned where they are subject to radiant heat, draughts or dampness, and the surrounding temperature should not exceed 35°C. They must also be checked with a spirit level to ensure that they have been mounted perfectly level—this is very important.

THE STANDARD PYROMETER

This consists of a galvanometer fitted with a temperature scale, a thermocouple housed inside a porcelain sheath, and two pieces of compensating cable for connecting the two. All brackets and fixing instructions are normally provided.

Installation is simple—the metal framework of a kiln is often drilled by the manufacturer at a position suitable for the installation of a thermocouple. All that is necessary is to extend the hole through the brickwork (easy: the brickwork is very soft) and push the thermocouple into the hole as far as it will go (the metal flange of the thermocouple will then be up against the metal sheeting of the kiln and the thermocouple tip will be projecting into the firing chamber). The galvanometer is connected, by the flanges provided, on to the side or roof of the kiln, and the compensating cables are connected between the terminals of the thermocouple and the two terminals on the instrument, making sure that the red wire is connected to the red terminals and black to black. A screw fitted to the front or just underneath the front of the instrument can then be adjusted to set the instrument reading to the room

Fig. 36. Standard indicating pyrometer

temperature, or, more precisely, the actual temperature inside the kiln (i.e. normally about 18°C).

Prices for a pyrometer to indicate temperatures up to 1300°C vary from £16 to £30 depending upon the length of thermocouple necessary to pass through the kiln wall. A 1300°C indicating pyrometer for Podmore P.1–P.9 kilns costs, for example, £19 10s. Cheaper pyrometers to operate at lower kiln temperatures (1100°C) can be obtained as the thermocouple wires can then be made of a cheaper grade of metal, or metals other than platinum.

THE THERMOLIMIT

This is sometimes referred to as a Pyrolimit. It consists of the same type of thermocouple as is used for the standard pyrometer and the same compensating cable. The instrument is, however, much more sophisticated.

The instrument is usually of the potentiometric type and carries a temperature scale on a bigger dial (7 inches) than the standard pyrometer (4 inches). In addition to the temperature-indicating pointer (normally black in colour) the instrument also has a further pointer (normally red) which can be manually set to any position on the scale. The black pointer indicates

Fig. 37. Thermolimit and controlling pyrometer instrument

the temperature inside the kiln at all times but when this indicating pointer reaches the setting at which the red pointer has been manually fixed the instrument is automatically cut off, which in turn cuts off the electricity supply to the kiln, and firing therefore stops.

The price of a Thermolimit varies but is generally from about £53, depending upon the size of the kiln and the electrical fitments already present in the kiln.

THE CONTROLLING PYROMETER

This is very similar in design to the Thermolimit but incorporates extra circuits which enable the instrument to act as a thermostat, if necessary, to maintain the kiln at one particular temperature, which is preset by a manual setting of the red pointer referred to in the description of the Thermolimit.

The instrument is fitted with a two-position switch which is referred to as a "soak–off" switch. When the switch is set to its "soak" setting the instrument will act as a thermostat once the temperature-indicating pointer reaches the setting of the manually fixed red pointer and the supply to the kiln elements is therefore switched on and cut off to regulate the temperature at the temperature indicated by the red pointer. If, however, the switch is set to the "off" position the instrument will function like a Thermolimit and automatically switch off the kiln when the black indicating pointer reaches the red one.

It is occasionally desirable to keep the ware at a certain temperature for a short period of time and the controlling pyrometer would obviously enable this to be done when the "soak–off" switch is set at its "soak" setting. If the kiln is at its preset temperature and needs to be switched off, all that is necessary is to move the switch to the "off" setting when the kiln will switch off automatically. Moving the switch to the "off" setting before the temperature of the kiln has reached the temperature preset by the red pointer will not, of course, result in the kiln switching itself off—it will only do this when the black pointer reaches the setting of the red one.

Controlling pyrometers are generally slightly more expensive than Thermolimits, costing about £57 upwards, depending upon the electrical fitments already fitted to the kiln and the kiln size.

A complete instruction book is always supplied with the instrument. The installation notes given for the Thermolimit apply also to this instrument.

THE TEMPERATURE REGULATOR

The thermocouple section is identical with those used for the other pyrometric instruments, but the instrument is not fitted with a temperature-indicating pointer and is therefore much more robust in its ability to withstand knocks and jolts.

The face of the instrument is fitted with a control knob which can be rotated within a scale graduated up to 1400°C. When the kiln is switched on, no matter how quickly the temperature rises it will never exceed the temperature indicated on the scale by the control knob. The temperature regulator therefore functions exactly like a thermostat fitted into the oven circuit of an electric cooker and, like a cooker thermostat, is fitted with a relay to switch the electricity supply on and off.

Two indicating lights are often fitted to the instrument: one of these lights up only when the temperature regulator is allowing current to pass to the elements, the other lights up only when the supply to the elements is cut off. One or other of the lights is therefore always on.

Fig. 38. Temperature regulator
This one is fitted with a maximimum scale reading of 450°C but instruments reading up to 1400°C are supplied for pottery purposes.

The price of one of these instruments is about £30 to £50, depending upon whether a contactor is already fitted to the kiln.

I have never been able to understand why this instrument is not much more popular than it is. Perhaps the suppliers are at fault for not advertising it more or perhaps we are all so accustomed to using instruments having moving pointers to indicate temperature continuously that this disadvantage of the temperature regulator is allowed to overshadow completely its compensating advantages. As there is not the delicate mechanism involved in the operation of a moveable pointer, the instrument is considerably more robust than other types of pyrometers. It enables the kiln operator to maintain the kiln easily at any temperature until it is switched off and it is possible to approximate the temperature of the kiln, if necessary, by moving the knob setting and "searching" until a setting is reached at which the lights on the instrument begin to switch on and off alternately. The price, too, is very competitive.

THE PROGRAMME CONTROLLER

This instrument is supplied with aluminium templates or cams which are marked with time and temperature co-ordinates. It is therefore easily possible to work out a suitable firing cycle within the capabilities of the kiln and plot this on one of the aluminium cams (drawing a continuous line on the cam very much as one would draw the performance line on a graph), to denote the required rate of temperature increase, maximum temperature, and rate of cooling, etc. The cam is then cut to the contour denoted by the line drawn upon it, and the cam template fitted to the instrument.

The instrument is fitted with a motor which can be switched on and off by means of a switch. When the motor is switched on, the spindle upon which the cam is fitted is caused to rotate very slowly (one revolution per twenty-four hours or so), thus turning the cam with it. As the cam very slowly turns it deflects a guide (called the cam follower) which is in constant contact with the edge of the cam and as the cam follower itself is connected to a pointer on the temperature scale of the instrument a deflexion of the cam follower causes a deflexion of the instrument pointer.

This pointer is a "regulating" pointer but there is also another pointer which denotes the actual temperature inside the kiln; but provided the firing cycle indicated by the shape of the cam is within the capabilities of the kiln the two pointers will move in unison up and down the scale when the kiln is firing. The actual temperature inside the kiln, incidentally, is never allowed to exceed the temperature indicated by the regulating pointer, owing to a thermostat control which would automatically be brought into operation.

It will therefore be seen that the shape of the cam controls the rate of heating or cooling of the kiln and thus it is possible to pre-plan any required firing cycle and to use the instrument to put this planned cycle into practice, the instrument being controlled in accordance with the programme denoted by the shape of the cam. Naturally the cam must be set and tightened in a position which causes the indicating instrument to read room temperature (or the temperature inside the kiln

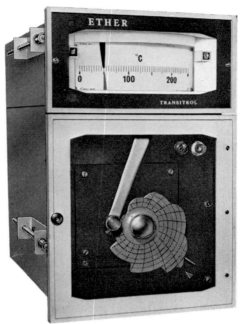

Fig. 39. A programme controller

if this is different from room temperature) before the motor is switched on and the kiln firing started.

Note that the cam will only be driven by the instrument motor while the motor switch is in its "on" position; if the motor is switched off while the kiln is firing, the temperature inside the kiln (which will be indicated on the instrument) will remain constant and will not alter unless the motor is switched on again, which would start the cam rotating.

If the cam is rotated until the instrument registers, say, 1100°C, and the kiln switched on but the motor switch left in the "off" position, the kiln will increase its temperature at the quickest possible rate until it reaches 1100°C. At this point the kiln temperature will be kept constant until switched off manually or until the instrument motor switch is switched on.

Limit switch

A switching device is incorporated into the instrument which can be manually set to switch off the instrument and the kiln automatically at any desired temperature. An arrow is printed on the face of the instrument and the instrument automatically switches off when the limit switch lever rotates to a position opposite the arrow.

The lever itself is fitted to the spindle (arbor) upon which the cam is fitted and if, say, one wished the kiln to cut off automatically once a temperature of 1100°C had been reached after following a certain firing cycle, the procedure would be as follows.

Fit the cam on to the cam arbor and then rotate the cam until the reading on the instrument shows 1100°C. Hold the cam firmly in position and move the limit switch lever until this is opposite the arrow. Tighten the knurled knob on the cam arbor to clamp the limit switch lever firmly into position relative to the cam. When the cam is now rotated back into its starting position the limit switch lever will, of course, move back with it and when the kiln is switched on, and also the motor switch, the cam and limit switch lever will be driven around the scale, the limit switch lever reaching the cut-out arrow when the temperature inside the kiln is 1100°C.

These instruments will control the complete firing cycle and this would be particularly useful, for example, when attempting to produce kiln load after kiln load of pieces of the same colour, for the programme controller will ensure that successive firings are very similar to each other and thus a matching colour can be obtained from each firing.

As programme controllers will do virtually everything required in kiln firing they are very sophisticated instruments and are, consequently, the most expensive instruments normally used by studio potters. Prices range from £110 to £300 depending upon whether a contactor is already fitted to the kiln. A complete instruction book is provided with the instrument.

7 Choosing your Kiln

The choice of the correct kiln is influenced by five major factors—

(a) The approximate size of the kiln required.

(b) The maximum temperature to which the kiln will be fired.

(c) Difficulty of access to the kiln site.

(d) Whether the electricity consumption of the kiln can be accommodated by the existing electricity supply.

(e) The space in which the kiln is to be situated.

OPTIMUM SIZE, ACCOMMODATION, ETC.

The approximate size of the kiln required can only be determined by the prospective buyer. He alone knows the size and quantity of the pots which are to be produced and fired. The pottery teacher, however, has a particularly difficult decision to make for he has to estimate the output of a class rather than of an individual, and this is no easy task. If you must err then err on the right side: always select the kiln that is likely to be too large rather than one which is likely to be too small. There can be nothing more distressing for the pottery student than finding that the ware he has taken perhaps days or weeks to produce to the firing stage cannot be fired immediately because the kiln is too small, resulting in a build-up of ware to be fired. It may be of some help to know that the most popular size of kiln for use in schools is one with interior dimensions of 15 × 15 × 18 inches. This is a reasonably sized kiln, large enough to cope with the largest pieces likely to be produced by pottery students. The decision on the correct size of kiln does, however, have to be tempered by common sense: a large pottery class of, say, forty or fifty students will need a considerably larger kiln than a small one of perhaps ten or twenty students. The more ambitious studio potter and the larger pottery classes will need kilns which are considerably larger than 15 × 15 × 18 inches, and kilns with interior dimensions of 18 × 18 × 24 inches, and even larger, are quite commonly used.

There are, of course, several different types of elements which can be used for electric furnaces. Generally speaking, the higher the temperature to which the kiln will have to be fired the more expensive the elements become. If you are not likely to fire to a higher temperature than 1000°C then Nichrome elements could be used. These are considerably cheaper than the Kanthal A elements which are used in kilns having a maximum firing temperature of 1200°C. If higher temperatures than these are required for stoneware work then Kanthal A1 elements will be necessary—and these are more expensive than the Kanthal A type. There are, incidentally, other grades of Kanthal wire which are sometimes used for pottery kiln elements. The A and A1 grades, however, appear to be those in most popular usage.

In addition to the more expensive elements required for high temperatures, more expensive refractory bricks have to be used. For this reason the low-temperature kilns fitted with Nichrome elements cannot be converted to high-temperature ones merely by changing the type of elements as the kiln brickwork will not be capable of withstanding the increased temperature. Kilns fitted with Kanthal A elements, however, are often fitted with bricks which withstand temperatures well over 1300°C, and thus it is usually possible to fit a set of Kanthal A1 elements and convert the kiln for these elevated temperatures.

Studio electric kilns are generally supplied in unit form. This is to say that they are supplied in one complete unit rather than in prefabricated form—bits and pieces to be assembled together. Pottery kilns are comparatively heavy pieces of equipment (for example, a kiln with internal dimensions 15 × 15 × 18 inches is likely to weigh between 4 and 6 hundredweight) and care should be taken to ensure that the kiln required can be easily moved from the delivery point to the actual site where the kiln is to be installed. The writer knows of one or two instances where kilns have been purchased and delivered to schools and studio potteries and then it has been found that the kilns were too large to pass through doorways or to be negotiated down flights of steps, etc. If the access to the kiln site gives a very difficult approach then the only alternative may be for the kiln to be supplied in prefabricated form. Most kiln suppliers would be only too pleased to offer a quotation for doing this but, as can be appreciated, the cost of supplying the kiln in this form is considerably higher than the cost of a kiln supplied as one complete unit. Not only is the cost of building the kiln in "split-cabinet" or prefabricated form greater but it is necessary for the kiln manufacturer to send engineers with the kiln to build it on site.

The fourth major factor to be taken into consideration is the electricity supply to which the kiln will be fitted. Most kilns, like domestic electric cookers, have to be wired into the electricity supply. A kiln of interior dimensions $15 \times 15 \times 18$ inches, such as the Podmore P.5, has a rating of 6·75 kilowatts and takes, for example, 28 amperes on a single-phase circuit. Larger kilns take considerably more—for example, a kiln of interior dimensions $18 \times 18 \times 24$ inches with a rating of 12 kilowatts will take a current of about 50 amperes if it is wired into a single-phase 240 volt supply line, or about 17 amperes on each leg of a three-phase circuit. Most housing estates have three-phase electricity cables from which single-phase lines are taken and fed into each house, although industrial concerns often have a three-phase supply passed directly into the factory to a sub-station from which emanate the single-phase lines to each department. All this perhaps seems rather complex and the prospective buyer is strongly recommended to discuss this with his local Electricity Board. Their engineers are generally very helpful and would be able to advise whether the kiln under consideration could be wired into the existing electricity supply without the addition of further cables. Putting in additional cable can be a fairly expensive business if the cable has to be of considerable length.

Finally, the last major factor to be taken into consideration is the space in which the kiln will be situated. There should be at least sufficient space to allow the sides of the kiln to be 6 inches away from any wall with enough space between the back of the kiln and the wall to give working space for any overhauls or replacing of elements. In actual practice the rear of the kiln is often pushed within 6 inches of a wall but provision is made for the kiln to be moved forward again if access to the rear is required. Front-loading kilns will, of course, demand a little more floor space than top-loading kilns because of the space needed for the door or doors to swing open and the working space needed to load the kiln from the front, etc., and if floor space is very limited a top-loading kiln may be the only answer. Top-loading kilns have their advantages but they also have some important disadvantages. Whilst they offer easy loading when one is placing pots on to the base of the kiln, if a shelf has to be placed above this bottom layer of pots there is a risk of grit, etc., falling or rubbing off the shelf while it is being placed into position, on to the pots below. The upward-lifting door can also prove heavy to handle and if the door stay is not made secure and the door should slip, serious damage could result to the kiln, to you, or to both.

The ceiling of the room in which the kiln is situated should be several feet above the kiln, especially if the ceiling is of wood construction. Electric kilns do not constitute a fire hazard but common sense dictates that it is best not to have inflammable materials immediately on top of the kiln. Most kilns, incidentally, do not attain an external temperature greater than 120–140°C during normal pottery firings, the hottest point usually being at the kiln door and the coolest at the rear of the kiln.

COST OF FIRING

This can very approximately be estimated by multiplying the kilowatt rating by the cost of one unit of electricity and then multiplying this by the length of time required to fire the kiln before switching off.

For example, if one is using a kiln having a rating of 6 kilowatts and the cost of a unit of electricity is, say, $1\frac{1}{2}$d. then the cost of firing the kiln for *one* hour will be approximately 9d. If such a kiln was fired to 1100°C and it took eleven hours to reach this temperature, then the cost of the complete kiln firing would be approximately 8s. 3d.

These figures, however, would only be applicable if the kiln was being fired at its maximum rate of temperature increase. If the kiln is being fired at a rate that is less than the maximum rate of which it is capable—such as would happen, for example, if a Sunvic energy regulator was fitted and this was set at a point below its maximum setting—the kiln elements would not be on all the time and the cost of firing would, therefore, be less than that indicated.

CARRIAGE AND DELIVERY

As has been previously mentioned, kilns are normally delivered as one complete unit and they would normally be transported from the manufacturers to your address by one of many road haulage companies. It should be appreciated that in those instances where the kiln is handed from the supplier to a haulage company, the haulage company will usually arrange for the lorry carrying the kiln to be loaded with several other items and classes of goods which are to be delivered to the same area. This is quite reasonable for it is obviously uneconomical for the haulage company to send out a large lorry loaded merely with one kiln. This could be done but the cost to deliver would be ridiculously high: the greater the number of orders despatched on one lorry the less will be the carriage charge per order. The haulage company's lorries are therefore loaded with perhaps a dozen or more consignments to different customers and it will be appreciated that it can be difficult for the haulage company to give a precise time at which their lorry will reach the premises of any one customer concerned. The most accurate delivery time that one can expect to be given is consequently an estimated one of, say, in the morning, or in the afternoon, of any particular day.

Many kiln manufacturers, however, deliver kilns on their own vehicles and would be prepared to give an estimation of the cost upon request. Delivery by the kiln manufacturer's vehicle obviously has several advantages but it should also be remembered that the cost of carriage generally tends to be appreciably more than the cost of carriage charged by independent haulage companies, British Road Services or British Rail. A further point to remember is that delivery by the kiln manufacturer's vehicle may have to be delayed by several days or more if the customer's address is a considerable distance away from the manufacturer. This is due to the fact that to keep carriage costs to reasonable proportions, the kiln manufacturer may have to wait until he has two or three kilns to deliver in the same area: the total cost involved in sending the delivery vehicle can then be divided proportionally to each customer's kiln.

When in doubt about delivery or off-loading arrangements, always ask the kiln supplier for advice.

8 Basic Effects of Heat on Clay

With the exception of some terracottas and a few stoneware clays most of the clays used by potters are not merely clays dug up from the ground and purified but are mixtures of different types of clay with other materials mixed in to give other desirable properties. Generally most prepared clays are made from a mixture of two or three different types of ball clay, two or three different types of china clay, flint, and Cornish stone, all of which are mixed together, in liquid form, in carefully controlled amounts. The mixture is then sieved and passed over powerful magnets before being passed to the filter presses, where surplus water is removed to convert the clay from its liquid state to a plastic condition (i.e. with the consistency of Plasticine). This plastic clay is then passed through a pug mill where the clay is thoroughly sliced and mixed to give it a very homogeneous consistency. Prepared clay is generally referred to as a "body" rather than as a clay, and particularly so once the clay has been fired.

VITRIFICATION AND POROSITY

Potters speak of some clays as being more refractory than others; by this, of course, they mean that the firing temperature or maturing range is higher for certain clays than others—for example, stoneware bodies which have to be fired at temperatures of about 1250–1300°C are more refractory than earthenware ones which fire at 1100–1150°C. Potters also speak of "vitrification" and "porosity," which are terms used to describe the degree of water retentivity of the body after firing. A vitrified body is one that is dense and non-porous, or nearly so, i.e. its porosity is low. A body having a high porosity is one which is very porous. The porosity of a body generally decreases as it is fired to higher temperatures.

A body is correctly fired when it has been fired to its maximum degree of vitrification without deforming or has been fired to a temperature which has enabled the body to develop a sufficient coefficient of contraction to enable glazes to be used without crazing (more about this later). The temperature or, more correctly, the range of temperatures at which this stage is reached varies from one type of body to another and is referred to as the firing range, maturing range, or vitrification point of the clay. Some clays, e.g. stoneware, will be almost completely vitrified when this point has been reached, others will possess an appreciable degree of porosity—such as the earthenware and terracotta types.

Each of the constituents of prepared pottery clays plays a different role. The ball clays are generally introduced to make the body plastic and to give it good workability. China clays are generally introduced to add whiteness to the body and are generally a little more refractory than ball clays. Flint, as we shall see later, supplies silica and is introduced mainly to develop craze-resistance, and stone serves as the flux which melts and holds the other particles together. When the clay has been fired it should not be considered as one homogeneous mass but more as a mixture of different materials suspended in a fluid which has become solid on cooling to hold all the particles firmly in position. Other materials are very frequently used in bodies, for example, felspar or nepheline syenite is often used as a substitute for Cornish stone, and quartz or even sand is sometimes used as a substitute for flint.

Pottery should always be dry before being fired. This is a golden rule. If damp pottery is placed into the kiln there is a great risk of its cracking or literally exploding during the firing operation, and bits would be scattered over all adjacent pottery pieces, probably damaging them. A good way of determining whether clay ware is dry is to place it against the cheek. If it feels cold then the ware is damp and must be dried for a further period of time. Thick pieces of pottery take longer to dry than thin pieces and they also take longer to fire. If you place thick and thin pieces of pottery into the same kiln the kiln would have to be fired a little more slowly than would be the case if one were firing thin pieces only.

When clay is fired it undergoes several complex changes and, even though it is dry when being placed into the kiln, a considerable amount of water vapour will be driven off during the firing operation. This volume of water driven off may be about fifty times the volume of the kiln and is not water which can be dried away before firing. This is water which is chemically held by the clays present in the body. All clays, of course, shrink as they are being dried and they shrink still further during the firing operation. This degree of shrinkage varies from clay to clay but is generally higher in those bodies which have the higher firing temperatures. The more clay present in the body the greater will be the degree of shrinkage.

THE IMPORTANCE OF SILICA

Silica is possibly the most important material used in ceramics—it is indeed sometimes regarded as the basis of the pottery industry and it is fortunate for the potter that the majority of the earth's crust contains supplies of silica in one form or another. Flint pebbles found in the chalky strata of parts of southern England are traditionally used by the British potter to introduce silica into the body recipe after the pebbles have been calcined (i.e. burned) and crushed and ground to a powder. In other parts of Europe, and in America, quartz or sand is used for the same purpose. Silica also occurs abundantly in volcanic rocks and consequently also in clays, the decomposition product of volcanic rocks, and in sandstone.

As far as the potter is concerned the most important characteristic of silica is its behaviour when heated. Just as silica can be located in so many different materials so does the silica crystal itself occur in several different forms or modifications. When silica is heated some of it changes from one form to another only to revert to the original form when it is subsequently cooled. Other modifications of silica change permanently to another form and this new form remains when the silica is cooled.

MODIFICATIONS OF SILICA

The most important crystal modifications of silica are as follows—

α (alpha) quartz	β (beta) quartz
α (alpha) tridymite	β (beta) tridymite
α (alpha) cristobalite	β (beta) cristobalite

Of these the alpha and beta quartz and the alpha and beta cristobalite modifications are of particular concern. Whenever these silica forms change from one modification to another under the influence of heat, an expansion takes place; similarly when the silica is subsequently cooled and beta quartz, for example, reverts to its original form of alpha quartz, a contraction of the silica mass takes place.

Let us now look at this behaviour in more detail. When silica

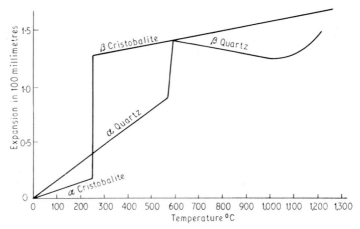

Fig. 40. Thermal expansion of silica minerals

is heated it gradually expands until a temperature of approximately 225°C is reached, when it suddenly expands very considerably as the alpha cristobalite content changes to beta cristobalite, which of course has the same chemical composition but a larger volume. As heating is continued another sudden expansion occurs at a temperature of approximately 550–575°C, when alpha quartz changes to beta quartz.

However, as heating continues other forms of silica begin to change into beta cristobalite, this conversion progressing with increasing rapidity as the temperature is raised higher. If silica is heated above 1200°C for example, most of it is converted into beta cristobalite. Thus the higher the temperature to which a pottery clay or body is fired, the more cristobalite is developed. This is a very important phenomenon.

As silica is cooled it gradually contracts until a temperature of approximately 575–550°C is reached, at which point the beta quartz content reverts to its original alpha quartz form accompanied by a sudden contraction. As the silica is cooled still further the point at which beta cristobalite changes back to alpha cristobalite is reached when the temperature drops to approximately 225°C. This beta to alpha cristobalite change causes another sudden volume contraction.

These sudden expansions at certain temperatures when the silica is heated and the sudden contractions at the same temperatures when it is cooled occur every time the silica, or a body containing silica, is fired. They therefore occur during glost firings as well as biscuit ones and if heating or cooling of the pottery is proceeding too quickly the stresses set up by the above silica "inversions" can, and often do, result in cracks right through the pottery causing the fault known as "dunting."

The formation of an appreciable amount of cristobalite renders pottery clays and bodies craze-proof. This is because the beta to alpha cristobalite change as the glost-fired ware is being cooled suddenly shrinks the biscuit ware, causing the glaze covering it to be placed in a state of compression.

STAGES IN BISCUIT FIRING

1. *Water smoking*
This covers the period from the beginning of the firing up to a temperature of about 150°C. During this period any remaining mechanically held water present in the clay is boiled away. Removal occurs in two ways: firstly, the body continues to contract until each particle touches its neighbour and, secondly, water is removed from between the particles.

2. *Dehydration period*
This covers an approximate temperature range of from 150°C up to 600°C. The chemically combined water present in the clay mostly comes away from the body between about 200°C and 460–600°C, but traces are still present up to 900°C. During this period of time the amount of steam given off from the ware will be about fifty times the interior volume of the kiln and this must be allowed to escape easily from the

kiln. If the kiln is heated too quickly from the commencment of firing up to the end of the dehydration period then steam formed inside the body may not be able to get to the surface quickly enough and may build up to such a pressure that the pottery is blown apart. Firing should therefore be at a fairly slow rate over this temperature range.

3. *Oxidation period*
This is at 400 to 900°C, when most of the carbon present in the clay ware burns away. If this oxidation of the carbon content is not done completely the result may be the formation of what is referred to as a black core inside the body. This can sometimes be seen on building bricks and insufficient oxidation can also result in small black holes being formed on the surface of pottery or the glaze on bone china becoming green.

Incidentally, by 800°C the clay is as porous as a sponge as it has now lost all of its chemically held water and most of the carbon without any readjustment of the other ingredients. At this stage the body is, in fact, lighter in weight than it was when first placed into the kiln and it is extremely porous. If the tip of the tongue is touched against the pottery the tongue will stick because of the suction caused by the biscuit absorbing moisture from the tongue. This phenomenon is used by experienced industrial potters to give a very rough guide as to whether the biscuit ware has been fired to a high enough temperature. If the biscuit is too porous it has not been fired hard enough, if too vitreous it has been overfired.

4. *Vitrification period*
This covers a temperature range from about 900°C up to the firing temperature of the clay. The fluxes present in the body now begin to react with the clays and tend to soften and as the temperature is increased they begin to melt more and more until eventually, if the temperature were taken beyond the vitrification point of the body, gases would be given off which would lead to bloating or blistering. When this happens the fluxes in the body would be literally boiling.

9 Basic Effects of Heat on Glazes

Glazes are suspensions in water of materials which will subsequently melt together to form a glass-like material.

MATCHING OF GLAZES

Glazes have to be "matched" to the body to which they are applied if good craze-resistance is to be obtained: by this we mean that the rate of expansion and contraction of the glaze must be similar to that of the body otherwise one will obviously crack away from the other if the fired pot is suddenly heated or cooled. The rate of expansion of a glaze depends upon the quantity and rate of expansion of each material used in its composition. Various materials have very different rates and by a careful selection process it is possible, within limits, to design a glaze to have a specific rate of expansion and contraction. If the rate of expansion of the body is known, a glaze can therefore be calculated to suit it and this glaze would then be said to be "matched" to the body. In actual fact the glaze is designed so as to have a slightly lower coefficient of expansion than the body upon which it is to be used so that during the cooling of the glaze it contracts a little less than the body which therefore "squeezes" it, i.e. the contraction of the body puts the glaze into a slight amount of compression. This then gives the glaze a built-in resistance against crazing.

EUTECTICS

Some very strange things can happen when materials are heated, and glaze constituents are no exception. Silica, for example, which is a constituent of nearly all glazes, has a melting point of 1713°C and is therefore a very refractory (i.e. heat-resisting) material. However, when this is mixed with other materials and melted in the kiln, it combines with the other materials to form new compounds which together have a much lower melting-point—very often lower than the melting-points of any of the materials in the original mixture. This formation of "eutectics" (i.e. mixtures which have a melting-temperature lower than that of any of their constituents) may seem very surprising but it is nevertheless true.

When a glaze is heated, the materials from which it is made begin to combine together well before the glaze becomes completely molten. The glaze itself gradually melts and becomes increasingly more molten as heating is continued, until eventually it becomes so fluid that it runs almost like water. When the glaze is cooled it becomes progressively more viscous until, at a temperature of approximately 800–600°C, depending upon the type of glaze, it becomes rigid and ceases to flow.

It would not be strictly true to refer to the glaze as now being a solid. Solids have definite melting points: lead, for example, suddenly melts at a temperature of 327°C, copper melts at 1084°C, and once the temperature drops below their melting-points these materials become solid again. Glazes, like glasses, are known as supercooled liquids which are solid at normal temperatures—they do not have a definite melting-point but gradually soften over a wide range of temperature.

BUFFER LAYER

As the glaze becomes more and more molten it increasingly attacks the body to which it is applied. This reaction between the body and the glaze is very important for it results in a layer which is part glaze and part body, which we call the "buffer layer" and which helps to fix the glaze firmly to the body. Instead of having a definite layer of glaze upon a definite body—rather like a sheet of water upon a block of aluminium, we have a layer of glaze which merges with a buffer layer of part glaze part body which merges with the body. A good buffer layer helps to anchor the glaze and thus helps to prevent the glaze cracking away, as happens in crazing or peeling.

If the biscuit ware has not been properly fired so that excess gases are given off during the glost firing, these gases can dislodge the glaze film and rupture it. When this happens the glaze may roll back to leave a bare patch—the fault known as crawling. Grease, dust, or dirt on the biscuit ware can cause the same fault.

BUBBLES AND CRATERS IN GLAZE

During the heating of a glazed article gases escape not only from the body but obviously also from the glaze itself as this decomposes under the influence of heat. When the glaze begins to melt, the escape of these gases becomes increasingly difficult until the gases eventually have to bubble their way through the molten glaze. The speed with which they do this varies from glaze to glaze and depends upon the thickness and fluidity of the glaze layer, but when they eventually do reach the surface they burst and this results in the formation of small craters. The purpose of subsequent heating of the glaze is to enable it to become just sufficiently fluid for it to flow and fill in these craters. If the glost firing is done very rapidly the gas bubbles can be trapped inside the glaze as there is not sufficient time for them to escape through the molten glaze before the kiln is switched off and the glaze becomes solid again. Furthermore, because the glaze would not become sufficiently fluid to allow the craters to be filled in, the glaze would have a pinholed appearance. To achieve a nice smooth glaze surface, free of bubbles and blemishes, it is therefore often necessary to fire the kiln comparatively slowly just before it has reached the recommended firing temperature for the glaze being used, or alternatively to hold the kiln at its firing temperature for half an hour or so.

STRESSES AND STRESS RELEASE

While the glaze is molten some of the constituents are being vaporized and if this were allowed to continue unnecessarily the glossy glazes would become very dull and lack shine. As the glaze cools towards the point at which it becomes a solid mass this rate of vaporization decreases considerably. To obtain a good glossy glaze the kiln should therefore be cooled fairly quickly down to about 750°C, at which temperature most glazes will be rigid. Any stresses or strains created in the glaze by this rapid rate of cooling will be easily absorbed, for the glaze is molten and any stresses will just flow away. However, as the glaze becomes increasingly more rigid it becomes a very different story; the glaze is now able to crack—and will do so if stresses and strains are caused by cooling too quickly. It is therefore best to fix an arbitrary point of 750°C and to cool as quickly as possible down to this point followed by a much slower rate of cooling.

EFFECTS OF COOLING

Another fault known as "devitrification" can be caused by cooling the glaze too slowly while it is molten. This fault often results in a transparent glaze taking on a milky appearance. There are other causes, but slow cooling is a common one.

With matt and opaque glazes a very rapid cooling is never necessary and in fact with opaque glazes may hinder the development of the correct amount of opacity.

Once the temperature drops below 700°C care must be taken to ensure that the rate of cooling is slow enough to prevent the ware from cracking. There are two particularly dangerous temperature ranges—at about 575°C and at about 225°C. At these points, for technical reasons discussed in the previous chapter, the silica present in the body undergoes a sudden contraction as it is being cooled, with the result that the body and the glaze layer fixed to it suddenly contract. If all of the body and the glaze covering it reached these temperature points at the same time, and thus shrank at the same time, no problems would occur but this ideal state of affairs is never reached in practice. While one part of the pot may be at one of these critical temperature points, another part of the same pot may well be at a temperature 10, 20, 30 or even more degrees different. During the cooling operation the inside of the pot is, for example, usually hotter than the outside; similarly, during the cooling operation, the foot of a pot resting on the bat is usually hotter than the top of the same pot standing in free air, owing to the high amount of heat retained by the bat. These temperature differences inevitably produce strains which are so magnified by the sudden shrinkage of the pot when part of it reaches the critical temperature points mentioned above that cracking often takes place. These cracks, due to heat stresses, are known as dunts and usually penetrate right through the pot, thus making it fit only for the scrap heap.

To prevent this cracking taking place we must therefore allow the pot to absorb these stresses over as long a period of time as possible and this can only be done by cooling slowly when the temperature of the kiln approaches 575°C and again when the kiln temperature approaches 225°C.

10 Difference in Technique Between Craft and Industrial Potters

Pottery ware is normally processed in two firing stages, the first firing of the clay ware which is termed the "biscuit" fire and the subsequent fire of the glazed ware which is termed the "glost" fire.

EARTHENWARE, TERRACOTTAS, AND OTHER POROUS CLAYS

There is a considerable difference in technique between that practised by the craft potter and that carried out by his industrial counterpart. Studio or craft potters invariably fire the biscuit ware to a temperature just high enough to make the clay hard and of good porosity so that a good film of glaze is picked up during the dipping operation. This is subsequently followed by a glost firing to a higher temperature than that of the biscuit fire.

Industrial potters, on the other hand, invariably fire their clay ware to a temperature higher than that of the glazed ware. Clays, like glazes, have a range of temperature to which they must be fired if satisfactory results are to be obtained. Let us take a specific example, such as an earthenware or terracotta clay having a firing range of 1100–1150°C. Craft potters would generally fire this clay to a temperature of about 900–1050°C and then follow this with a glost firing to 1100°C or higher, which would serve to develop both the body and the glaze at the same time. Industrial potters, however, would fire these clays at a biscuit firing of 1100°C or higher, which would serve to develop the clay, and would then follow this with a glost fire using a glaze that matures at a lower temperature, say 1050°C.

The industrial technique definitely tends to give better results and certainly tends to develop more craze-resistance than the craft pottery technique. The only disadvantage is that after the biscuit firing the biscuit ware is comparatively vitreous (non-porous) and it is consequently much more difficult to pick up a good layer of glaze during the dipping operation. For this reason industrial concerns always go to great lengths to make sure that the glaze being used in the dipping tubs is of exactly the right consistency to ensure a satisfactory pick-up of glaze, and for really vitreous bodies the industrial potters use spraying techniques to apply the glaze coat, which overcomes the glazing problems associated with a non-porous body. The expense of installing spraying equipment is, however, very considerable and is usually beyond craft potters.

There are other advantages to be gained from the industrial practice of firing the biscuit fire higher than that of the glost. During the subsequent glost fire the body is comparatively inert since it has already been fired in the biscuit fire to a temperature higher than anything reached during the glost fire. With the craft pottery technique, once the temperature of the glost fire surpasses that of the biscuit, the body itself becomes much more reactive and gases are once again given off by the body which now have to bubble their way through the film of glaze covering it. This may result in pinholes or other glaze blemishes. This does not happen to anything like the same extent with the industrial technique and the appearance of the finished piece of pottery tends to be slightly superior to that produced by the craft potter.

Another advantage is that since the body will have been fired to its maturing point on the first fire any warping or distortion that is likely to take place will take place during this firing and not during the subsequent glost firing. If it was required to glaze a thin, pencil-like object, the industrial potter would do this by firing the clay to its maturing temperature during the biscuit fire, and during this time the object would be left lying flat on a bat or other suitable support to prevent distortion. During the glost fire, which would be at a lower temperature, the same object could be supported merely on its two ends with comparatively little risk of distortion. The craft potter, trying to fire the same piece, would find that it would distort very considerably during the glost fire unless it was supported at points other than at its ends, which would result in marks being left on the glost surface.

The craft potter forgoes all these advantages of the industrial technique in order that he may get a high porosity on the biscuit ware which enables him to apply the glaze very easily.

It should always be remembered that, provided one is using satisfactory glazes and bodies, the temperature to which the body is fired controls the degree of craze-resistance developed by the pottery ware. It is true that crazing difficulties can sometimes be overcome by firing the glost firing a little higher than was done with previous glost firings and it is generally assumed that the increased craze-resistance arises directly as a result of reactions in the glaze following the extra heat to which it has been subjected. This is not strictly true: the increased craze-resistance is also due to the increased amount of heat applied to the body via the glaze layer.

In addition to the two-fire method (biscuit and glost), pottery can also be fired by a one-fire process. This involves applying glaze to clay ware and then firing this once to a temperature which is high enough to develop both the body and the glaze at the same time.

STONEWARE AND PORCELAIN

The above comments refer, of course, to the firing of terra-cottas, buff clays, and all forms of earthenware. In addition to this it is necessary to fire bone china to the full maturing temperature during the biscuit firing as at this temperature of 1240–1280°C the bone china ware will deform so easily that it has to be placed on special setters or buried in calcined alumina, etc.; glazed bone china could not of course be treated in this way. Where stoneware and porcelain are concerned—and the special qualities of these bodies are being appreciated by more and more potters—the pots are so vitreous after being fired to a full biscuit maturing temperature that the craft potter would be faced with difficult application problems if he wished to apply glaze by a dipping process. With these bodies the craft potter therefore fires the body to a low biscuit temperature to give the porosity necessary for dipping his pottery successfully.

Stoneware and porcelain are therefore fired to a biscuit temperature of approximately 900 to 1000°C, after which they are quite porous and can be dipped quite easily. The glaze is then fired to a temperature of approximately 1220–1300°C.

The quality and texture of stoneware and porcelain glazes is, incidentally, often enhanced by the gases which inevitably bubble through from the biscuit ware and also by the reactions which take place between the glaze and the decomposing body. Indeed much stoneware pottery owes its success and appeal to the glaze effects brought about by a high-temperature glost firing.

11 Kiln Placing

The term "kiln placing" is a confusing one. It does not refer in any way to a movement of the kiln but to the act of placing pottery inside the kiln prior to firing. The name is almost certainly an abbreviation which has been handed down from generation to generation and consequently those people in industrial ceramics whose profession is continually placing pottery into intermittent kilns or on the trucks used for tunnel kilns, are referred to as "kiln-placers."

KILN FURNITURE: SHELVES AND PROPS

With the studio electric kiln the pottery is placed on shelves made up of from one to four kiln bats depending upon the size of the firing chamber. If elements are fitted into the hearth (base) of the kiln the pottery should not be placed directly on the hearth but on a kiln shelf placed $\frac{1}{2}$–1 inch clear of the base. This prevents possible damage to elements if a pot should break and in addition allows a more even heat distribution throughout the kiln. If the pots to be placed are comparatively small in size then several shelves may be needed and these are supported one above the other by kiln props. There are a few different types of kiln props but the most popular ones are castellated props and cast props. Castellated props are basically tubular but have interlocking turrets on them—rather like the battlements of a medieval castle or like the top of a castle used in a chess game. Cast props are usually solid cylinders which have a dome at one end and a recess at the other—into which fits the dome of the prop underneath. A number of small props, say 1 inch or $1\frac{1}{2}$ inches in height, will obviously make it possible to alter the distance between shelves with ease, but a series of props one above the other obviously do not give such a stable assembly as one large prop of the same height. Flat circular discs of a greater diameter than the kiln props are often placed between a kiln bat and the prop immediately below it as these help to spread the load on the shelf and reduce the risk of shelf collapse—particularly where there are two or more bats per shelf and one prop, or column of props, is supporting two bats.

An important point is that each bat should be supported at three points as this prevents the "rocking" which might occur if the bat was supported at each of its four corners—a three-legged chair or stool will never rock but a four-legged one might. The supports should be arranged in similar positions for each succeeding shelf so that the total weight of the complete set of kiln furniture acts downwards through continuous columns.

During biscuit firing the pottery shrinks considerably and if warping is to be avoided this shrinking action should not be arrested by any irregularity on the kiln shelf. The best way to assist this shrinkage is to place a thin layer of silver sand (silica sand) over the shelves as each particle of sand will act like a ball-bearing in assisting the contraction of the pot. During glost firing, however, a layer of silica sand on the kiln shelves may be something of a hazard as particles of sand may fall on to glazed pottery, leaving a rough speck, or they may cause a nuisance by sticking to the base of the glazed pot. However, during glost firing some buffer layer between the pot and the kiln shelf is desirable in case any particles of glaze have been left on the base of the pot which will glue the pot to the kiln shelf and thus either cause the pot to be destroyed or cause a piece to be plucked away when the pot is taken off the shelf after firing. The ideal material for putting on the shelves for glost firing purposes is a mixture of alumina and china clay or zircon and china clay mixed with water and painted on the shelves in the form of a wash so that it adheres quite firmly. Many companies sell a specially prepared mixture known as bat wash, which is quite cheap.

If the same kiln is being used for alternate biscuit and glost firings it is best not to use silica sand for biscuit firings but merely to rely on the bat wash used for glost firings, as the risk of contamination of the glazed pots from particles of silica sand is considerable.

In any case the kiln furniture should be checked after each firing and any loose particles of bat wash lightly brushed away. Spots of glaze sticking to the shelves must be chipped or ground away and the area painted over with a new layer of wash. Cracked kiln bats should either be discarded or, if the crack is a very fine one, supported by a prop placed underneath the crack. This regular check is important and should always be done.

Kiln shelves and props are usually made from sillimanite or a mixture of refractory materials similar to sillimanite. These materials are very refractory and will easily withstand stoneware temperatures although if one requires the kiln bats to withstand temperatures up to 1300°C without warping then it is best to select bats either ¾ or 1 inch thick; ½ inch thick kiln shelves are very popular but these are best reserved for temperatures below 1200°C. Kiln furniture made from silicon carbide (carborundum) can also be obtained. There is little doubt that silicon carbide kiln furniture is generally superior to the sillimanite types—it is stronger and has better heat conductivity for example—but it is extremely expensive and for this reason is seldom used.

Some potters make their own kiln bats from refractory clays such as crank mixture or fireclay and grog mixtures but these are never as strong as industrially manufactured bats of similar thickness. Home-made kiln furniture is often prone to premature or sudden failure.

BISCUIT KILN PLACING

Placing a kiln for a biscuit fire is simpler than placing one for the glost fire as all that is really necessary is to place the pots inside the kiln with the object of getting as many pots as possible into the smallest possible space. The firing of a kiln costs money and waste of space is, therefore, money thrown away. With the smaller kilns one does not have a very great deal of free space in which to design the best layout of the pots in order to obtain a high packing density but with the larger kilns one can often rearrange the pots placed on kiln shelves to obtain a more tightly packed arrangement. I have often found it helpful to have an area of the work bench, or floor, marked out to the exact dimensions of the placing area and including the exact positions of props, etc. If the layout of props is different on one shelf to the layout of the props on the next shelf then I have used a further full-size diagram drawn on to the bench or floor to simulate this alternative arrangement. When this is done the pots can be rearranged within this marked area much more easily than would be the case inside the kiln as one can, of course, view the pots from all directions and handle them with much more ease. Furthermore, the pots can be arranged in their firing positions while the kiln is actually in use so that when firing is finished all that is necessary is just to pick the pots from their position in the marked-out area and place them inside the kiln at their pre-planned position. This can save quite a lot of time and prevent the breakage which can occur in moving the pots around inside the kiln.

When clay pots are fired they progressively shrink and will have a tendency to warp if the design of the pot does not give it adequate support and if the biscuit firing is taken up to the full maturing temperature of the clay, as should be done with earthenware and terracotta clays. Stoneware and porcelain should not be biscuit-fired to their maturing temperature of 1250–1300°C but should be fired to a lower temperature of 900–1100°C. Indeed some potters fire earthenware or terracotta and stoneware in the same kiln at the same time. Bone china ware should be fired to its full maturing temperature (around 1250°C), at which temperature it becomes semi-molten with the consequence that many of the pots are not capable of supporting themselves. Bone china clay ware therefore has to be placed in special setters to support the pots, or individual pieces are buried in a material such as calcined alumina from which the biscuit pots are taken after the firing and the particles of calcined alumina brushed or scoured off. Bone china plates are often stacked in piles of twelve or more with silica sand or a silica sand/alumina or china clay mixture between each two. This material supports the plates and prevents them from warping; the bottom plate, of course, is held in a setter. The placing and firing of bone china wares demands special placing procedures but as the use of this body is unusual among studio potters I do not propose to discuss this topic further but to refer to earthenware, terracotta, stoneware and porcelain wares.

In the biscuit fire, with all clays except bone china, it is permissible to place one pot inside another if this is at all possible. Thus a small bowl can be placed inside a larger one. Do not, however, make the error of packing too many pots inside another as the largest pot may give way during the firing—one should remember that for a short time during the biscuit fire the pots become weaker than they were when placed into the kiln. Only experience can determine the amount of weight that a certain pot is capable of holding. Clay pots can be placed upside down or on their side if this is helpful in obtaining tighter packing inside the kiln and if there is no increased risk of warping.

Large heavy pieces may need shrinkage platforms under them to prevent warpage. These are smooth slabs of clay made from the same clay as the pot and which shrink to the same extent as the pot. A thin layer of bat wash or silica sand should be placed between the shrinkage platform and the shelf to enable the clay platform to shrink easily without sticking to the shelf.

Closed-in shapes such as vases or teapots are comparatively easy to fire because their compact forms have a structural resistance to warping. Cups and bowls are more liable to warp and identical pairs of these are often "boxed" together, i.e. one on top of another (rim to rim) and stuck together by a gum such as gum arabic, which burns away during the firing. Thin pieces, of course, will warp much more easily than thick ones.

Finally, the cones should be placed into position and checks made to ensure that they are in a position directly in line with the spy-hole in the kiln door. Close the kiln door and you are ready to begin firing.

A most important point is that any clay ware placed into a kiln must be **DRY**. Damp ware is liable to crack or literally explode (thus damaging other pots), as a result of steam pressure built up inside it when firing begins. One way to check whether a pot is sufficiently dry is to hold it against the cheek: if it feels cold it is still damp; if no temperature difference can be felt it is probably dry enough to be fired.

GLOST KILN PLACING

Much more care must be taken with placing a kiln for the glost fire than for the biscuit fire as the glaze covering the pots will stick them together if they are allowed to touch. Similarly, should any glaze adhere to the underside of a pot

Fig. 41. Kiln furniture and placing accessories used for glazed ware

A. Pin Crank	E. Tubular Props	I. Saddles
B. Collar	F. Kiln Bat	J. Tile Crank
C. Cast Prop	G. Stilts	K. Tile Bat
D. Castellated Prop	H. Spurs	L. Tile Dots

such as on the foot or foot-ring of a saucer, this will stick the pot firmly to the kiln shelf if the pot is placed flat upon the shelf. Many pots *are* placed flat but the glaze is always removed from the base of the pot beforehand either by scraping, or, more usually, by using a sponge or a damp piece of felt. If the removal of glaze from the underside of a pot may be a little difficult or time-consuming, or if one may just want additional reassurance that no sticking is likely to occur then several different kinds of support can be used on which the pots can be placed to keep them clear of the kiln shelf. In Fig. 41 is an illustration of some of the more popular types of supporting items such as stilts, saddles, spurs, etc. These are quite inexpensive and it is false economy to continue to use them after several fires as the sharp edges of these items tend to become blunt after repeated firings. A new stilt, for example, will hardly leave a blemish on the base of a pot even if this is covered with a thin layer of glaze, whereas a stilt which has been in use for several firings may have the points removed and may have to be broken away from the base of the pot after firing, leaving unsightly marks which will have to be rubbed down.

Stilts and small saddles are particularly useful in the firing of glazed earthenware, terracotta, buff and bone china wares to support the pots clear of the kiln shelf, and a further advantage of using these is that the air circulation under the pots helps to reduce the temperature variation between the top and bottom of the pottery article. This will help to prevent the occurrence of cracking or dunting.

Have you ever noticed the three marks on the underside of a saucer between the rim and the foot ring? These are the three points at which the saucer was supported on special "cranks" during the glost fire in an industrial kiln. These cranks are refractory racks into which identical plates or saucers can be very tightly placed, and they are very extensively used throughout the ceramic industry. Podmores are the only supplier I know who can supply them in the small quantities needed by the studio potter. Pin cranks, as they are called, can only be used for glazed ware if the biscuit ware has been fired to a higher temperature as otherwise the plates or saucers placed inside the crank would warp during the glost firing. They can, therefore, be used to advantage with glazed earthenware, terracotta or bone china wares but not with stoneware or porcelain. Likewise the use of stilts, spurs or saddles can raise problems in the firing of stoneware or porcelain. If these wares are fired to the full maturing temperature, the pots may begin to sag or squat over the stilts or whatever supporting medium is being used, and for this reason stoneware and porcelain pots (which incidentally are often left unglazed at the base) are often stood directly on the kiln shelf—particularly with large pieces.

No matter how careful you are when placing the pots into the kiln you are likely to dislodge a few specks of dirt or bat wash and for this reason the top shelf should be placed first, followed by the shelves underneath. If any dirt is dislodged it will therefore fall downwards on to an empty shelf and not into or on to glazed ware. This procedure cannot, of course,

Fig. 42. Glazed pots supported inside the kiln

be followed with top-loading kilns as there is no alternative to placing the bottom deck of ware first (this is one of the disadvantages of a top-loading kiln).

Do make certain that any bat wash painted on the kiln shelves is quite dry before beginning to place ware into the kiln as it is surprising how damp bat wash gets on to the fingers and then on to the glazed pots. Incidentally, it is not usually necessary to give a complete coating of bat wash to the shelves after every firing but merely to "touch up" those areas from which traces of glaze deposited during the previous firing have been removed. Periodically it is a good idea to rub away the layer of bat wash with a flat grinding stone (not the Carborundum type) and then carefully to brush off the shelves, subsequently giving them a new coat of wash.

SOME POINTS TO REMEMBER

If you are firing earthenware, terracotta, etc., it is generally better to fire the biscuit fire to a higher temperature than that of the glost for the reasons discussed previously in Chapter 10. If this is not done, as is usual in the production of stoneware or porcelain where the clay ware is fired to about 900–1100°C and the glazed ware to 1250–1300°C, the ware during the glost firing will continue to shrink once the temperature to which the biscuit ware was fired has been exceeded. When placing stoneware pots for the glost fire one must bear in mind that further shrinkage is going to occur and this must be allowed for when placing the pots. Some kiln props are of a much wider diameter at the base than they are at their tip and pots can be placed so that they overhang the base of the prop. When these pots shrink it is sometimes possible for them to shrink down on to the kiln prop, with the result that they are stuck firmly after the firing has been completed.

If any kiln bats are cracked they should either be discarded or broken into two pieces for use as half bats, etc. If the crack is a minor one it is usually possible to make use of the bat with very little risk of failure, provided that a prop is used to support the bat immediately under the cracked area.

When placing ware for either biscuit or glost firing leave a gap of at least 1 inch between the pot and the nearest element. Failure to do this may result in one side of the pot being scorched.

When placing glazed ware into the kiln hold the pieces firmly; trying to hold pieces delicately with thumb and finger is much more likely to result in the glaze film becoming damaged—unless, of course, the pots are very small. If any is knocked away during the placing process then apply some more, either touched on with a finger or soft brush, followed by rubbing smooth when dry.

It is best to avoid as much as possible placing differently coloured glazed pots in the same firing. If this cannot be avoided then try to keep white and highly pigmented glazes, for instance black, as far away from each other as possible as volatilization of glaze from one pot can influence the colour of its neighbour to a very noticeable degree.

Don't forget the Staffordshire cones and do ensure that when they collapse they will not fall against a pot which has been placed too close to them—a point easy to overlook.

12 Biscuit Firing

Terracottas, earthenware, and other clays which are porous when fired to maturing temperature, should preferably be biscuit-fired to the maturing temperature of the clay, although many craft potters fire these clays also at the temperature range which should be used for stoneware and porcelain— i.e. 900–1100°C.

CLAY FIRING TEMPERATURES

It should be remembered that the firing temperatures of earthenware and terracotta clays varies with different types of these clays. Most earthenware types of clay have a firing range of 1100–1150°C, but the terracotta types can vary more widely: Podmore's B31 clay, for example, has a firing range of 1100–1150°C but their B33 clay has a firing range of 1020–1040°C and firing this clay to, say, 1120°C will cause it to become so vitreous that it is almost impossible to glaze in the normal way. If you were therefore to mix pots made with B33 clay with pots made from B31 and biscuit-fire them in the same kiln to 1040°C the B31 pots would be underfired and would consequently be prone to crazing, unless this ware were fired to 1100–1150°C during the subsequent glost firing.

The firing temperature of the clay must therefore be known, and with all clays except stoneware and porcelain the pottery should be fired to the stated firing temperature. With stoneware and porcelain fire to about 900–1100°C, as firing these clays much higher during the biscuit firing will make them too vitreous to glaze easily. If Staffordshire cones are being used in the firing, the ones selected should obviously be those corresponding to the required firing temperature.

During the period of time that the pottery is being fired several very complicated chemical reactions take place and the firing schedule should be such that these reactions can take place unhindered. For all practical purposes however, these reactions can be grouped into two phases: the first phase being the formation of steam and the second phase being the burning away of all the organic (carbonaceous) material present in the clay. As was explained in a previous chapter, most of the steam which is formed in the clay is generated over the first 100–300°C or so and firing should consequently be done comparatively slowly over this range. Most of the burning away of organic materials takes place immediately afterwards and continues up to about 900°C.

The most important of these two phases is the first one— the liberation of steam, as the rate of temperature increase of kilns is usually not so rapid that all the carbonaceous matter cannot be burned away. I know of many potters who merely take care over the first hour or so after the kiln is switched on and then allow the kiln to continue its temperature rise at a medium or high rate with apparently no ill effects. A lot does depend upon the kiln, the amount of ware inside the kiln and particularly the thickness of the ware being fired.

We will, however, assume that the pots to be fired are not thicker than ½ inch: this should cover 90 per cent of the pottery produced by school and studio potters. If the pottery is thicker than this then the rate of temperature increase of the kiln must be slower in order to allow the heat generated inside the kiln really to soak into the ware.

FIRING

After all your clay ware has been safely placed into the kiln and the kiln door closed you are ready to commence firing.

Heating up

First of all the vent plug should be removed and perhaps the spy-hole left open as well. If an energy regulator is fitted to the kiln this should be set at a fairly low setting; if the kiln is fitted merely with a three-position (low, medium, high) switch, then the switch should be set at its "low" position.

The object of this procedure is to ensure that during the early stages of firing the water vapour chemically held inside the clay, which is converted into steam, is allowed to escape from the kiln very easily. The rate of temperature increase should be fairly slow and certainly not greater than about

100 degrees per hour for the thinner pieces of pottery. The thicker pieces of pottery will demand a temperature increase considerably slower than this—perhaps as low as 50–70 degrees per hour.

The kiln will now gradually increase its temperature and large amounts of steam (which may not be seen) will be escaping from the vent-hole and spy-hole, of the kiln. After about 2–4 hours the kiln can be switched to its "medium" setting of the three-position rotary switch or, if an energy regulator is fitted instead of this, the regulator can be turned up to a reading of about "60" on the scale. At this point the temperature should be in the region of 150–350°C.

At the same time the vent plug can be placed firmly in position at the top of the kiln. If, however, there is a large amount of organic matter in the clay (this is generally so with stonewares and fireclays) or if the pots are very tightly packed inside the kiln, it may be better to delay putting the vent plug in position for a further hour or so. Alternatively, some potters place the vent plug across the hole for a short while so that the hole is not properly sealed. In any event kilns are not airtight and gases will escape even when the vent plug is firmly in position.

The actual brickwork lining the interior of the kiln will begin to glow a red colour at a temperature of about 600°C and at about 650–700°C will be glowing very noticeably. At this point the kiln will probably have been on medium setting for about 1–3 hours and it can now be switched to its high setting to finish off the firing for the terracotta and earthenware types of clay. For stoneware clays it is normally best to allow the kiln to remain for a further hour or so at its medium setting before switching to the high one, since many of these clays contain a comparatively high amount of carbon— particularly those with a fireclay content.

After switching to the high setting of the three-position switch or the 100 per cent setting of the energy regulator the kiln will now begin to increase temperature at its maximum speed. If experience shows that this rate of temperature increase is too rapid, then it may be best on future occasions to switch only to the 90 per cent setting of the regulator or less.

The kiln interior by now will be glowing brightly and after a further two or three hours the temperature will probably be in the region of 800–1000°C. If a pyrometer is fitted you will be able to determine the point at which you should start looking into the kiln to check the Staffordshire cones. This procedure should normally begin when the reading on the pyrometer gives an indication of some 30 degrees or so before the first cone is due to collapse. If a pyrometer is not fitted then one must rely upon glancing into the kiln through the spy-hole about every half-hour or so until the first cone begins to collapse. When this happens look into the kiln every ten minutes and switch the kiln off the moment the cone to which the ware is being fired has collapsed.

Cooling down
The rate at which kilns cool varies from model to model and naturally also depends upon the temperature and amount of ware and shelves inside the kiln. It is best to leave the kiln as it is until the interior temperature drops to about 100–150°C, when the door can be opened in stages.

Inspection
When the pots are taken from the kiln examine them closely. If any of them appear to be a greyish colour then there is probably still some organic matter inside them, in which case you will know that the temperature increase of future biscuit firings must be retarded by leaving the kiln on its medium setting for a longer period of time. If the pots are extensively cracked then one possible cause is that steam pressure built up inside the pot has had to rupture the pot to burst its way out. If this is the case then the kiln must be allowed to remain at its "low" setting for a longer period of time on future firings. Clay cracking, however, can be caused by a very "short" (i.e. not very plastic) clay or by working with the clay in too dry a condition, by not drying the pots evenly, or by drying them too quickly. In these cases the cracks will be present in the clay ware when placed into the kiln, although they may be so fine as not to be visible to the unaided eye; the biscuit firing will most certainly open them up, however.

SUMMARY

Most kiln manufacturers recommend an average rate of temperature increase of about 100° per hour except for the first two or three hours firing time where the rate of temperature increase must be slower than this. Comparatively thin pieces of pottery—say of a maximum thickness of $\frac{1}{4}$–$\frac{1}{2}$ inch—can be fired quite safely with this schedule, but very thick pieces— say thicker then $\frac{3}{4}$ inch—will need a lower firing rate, particularly in the early stages.

It is common practice to select a set firing cycle based upon experience of the first few firings and then to keep to this for all future firings for a similar type of ware. A typical firing schedule could well be as follows: "two hours on low with the vent plug out followed by inserting the vent plug and switching to medium for three hours followed by switching to high."

Schools particularly may have a problem in not having sufficient time to complete a firing. If this is so it is quite permissible with most kilns to leave the kiln at its low setting overnight as the kiln temperature will not rise above 400– 500°C at this setting. Then the following morning the kiln can be switched directly to its medium or high setting and the firing thus completed later in the afternoon.

As kiln manufacturers generally provide a graph with each kiln showing how quickly the kiln temperature will rise at various settings of the energy regulator or rotary switch it is possible to calculate roughly how long a firing to a certain temperature under a set firing procedure will take.

14 Reduction

In John B. Kenny's book *The Complete Book of Pottery Making* (Sir Isaac Pitman and Sons Ltd.) is related the story of a potter who lived in China many centuries ago and who specialized in making vases glazed with a green glaze containing copper oxide. His work was in constant demand and so he employed several assistants to maintain sufficient output. One day he loaded his kiln with ware, just as he had done so many times before, but when he came to light the fires he had considerable difficulty as he just couldn't get the fires to draw, thanks to insufficient draught in the chimney. Moreover, once he had the fires burning there was still a poor draught in his kiln and almost as much smoke escaped out of the firemouths as went up the chimney. Naturally the firing took considerably longer than usual and during all this time the air was filled with unpleasantly smelling smoke.

When the firing had finished the potter knew that much of his pottery would be ruined. Sure enough, pot after pot was taken out blackened and dull, and fit only for the scrap heap. However, right in the middle of his kiln was one pot the likes of which had never been seen before: it was a remarkably beautiful red colour.

Being a very patriotic sort of potter he decided that the Emperor should have it and so it was duly packed and despatched. The Emperor, in turn, was so delighted with it that he had the vase carefully broken and cut into small pieces which were then mounted on rings as though they were precious stones. Then he sent an order to the potter for more vases.

This was where the potter's troubles began: try as he might he just could not reproduce that vase. The Emperor, however, did not like to be kept waiting and demanded quick results. Still the potter tried but to no avail; nothing that he could do would produce more of those red vases. Eventually the Emperor could wait no longer and sent a message demanding quick results, or else!

The poor potter was terrified. Every experiment he had tried had failed but nevertheless he decided he would try once more and so he fired his kiln again. Half way through the firing the Emperor's messenger called again to threaten the potter with dire consequences if he did not produce the goods after this firing. This was simply too much for the poor potter who, deciding to end it all, opened the door of the kiln and jumped in.

His assistants rushed up but it was too late and all they could do was to close the dampers and wait for the kiln to cool. The kiln, however, had filled with an acrid smelling smoke which spread everywhere once the dampers were closed. Lo and behold, when the kiln was opened it was full of beautiful red coloured pots.

On subsequent firings the potters experimented with throwing dead animals on to the fire and closing the dampers slightly and they continued to obtain beautiful red pots. Eventually they tried wet straw, wood, etc., and still they obtained red-coloured pots. According to the legend this was how the secret of reduction was discovered.

EFFECT OF REDUCTION

A reduction atmosphere results when the kiln atmosphere becomes overloaded with carbon. When this happens sufficient oxygen cannot be obtained by the materials being burned to ensure their complete combustion. Under these conditions many compounds more or less fight between themselves to secure what small amount of oxygen is present in the reduction atmosphere, and thus many compounds in fact have their own oxygen content taken away from them. In this way green copper oxide loses some of its oxygen and becomes red copper oxide. Similarly red iron oxide loses some of its oxygen and becomes black iron oxide. The red colour produced by the reduction of copper oxide results in the beautiful *sang-de-bœuf* or ox-blood colour whereas black iron oxide formed by the reduction of red iron oxide can produce a greyish green colour known as celadon.

EFFECT ON ELEMENTS

So much has been said in the past about the great danger to electric kiln elements that it is commonly assumed that reduction either cannot be done, or cannot be done economically in an electric kiln. This is not necessarily so provided that certain basic pointers are observed. I have mentioned in an earlier chapter that the Kanthal elements used in most electric kilns, and for all those kilns fired over a temperature of 1150°C, are covered with a protective oxide layer when in use. This oxide layer is greyish in colour and serves to seal off the element metal itself from harmful gases in the kiln atmosphere which would otherwise seriously attack the metal thus reducing element life considerably. During a reduction firing this protective grey coating begins to reduce in thickness until eventually it disappears. However, usually two or three firings are necessary for this coating to be removed to such an extent that the element metal is showing through. This protective coating is restored to the elements after a normal firing—and by "normal" we refer to the usual oxidizing fire. It is therefore possible to create a reduction atmosphere in an electric kiln without excessively rapid element failure provided that the protective coating on the elements is not allowed to deteriorate seriously. In practice, it is usual to carry out a reduction firing and then to observe the element coating to see if the film is becoming thin. If there is any evidence of this then an oxidizing fire must be carried out to restore the coating to its usual thickness. It may take two or three oxidizing firings to restore the coating but, on the other hand, only one firing may be necessary. If the reduction atmosphere is not a very powerful one it may indeed be possible to carry out two or three reduction firings before an oxidizing fire is necessary. Reduction firings, then, can be carried out with electric kilns with reasonable economy provided that these elementary precautions are observed. Element life will certainly be reduced even if these precautions are observed but nowhere near as quickly as would be the case if reduction firings were carried out haphazardly.

I am often asked to give my opinion on how much element life will be reduced by reduction firings. How can I possibly answer a question like that? So much depends upon the length of the firing and the degree of atmosphere reduction, etc., as to make it impossible to give a positive answer. It is even impossible to give an estimated firing life for elements under normal oxidizing conditions—I have known elements to fail after a few months' use yet I have a friend in Tunbridge Wells who has been firing two or three times per week for eight years without ever needing a replacement element.

Even the element wire manufacturers cannot give any guidance on this point but the general feeling is that under conditions of reduction one can expect about half the element life obtained under oxidizing conditions—if that is anything to go by. However, the characteristic qualities of many reduced pots often enable the potter to demand higher prices than would otherwise be the case and this factor alone may more than compensate for the reduced element life.

So much for the practicability of reduction atmospheres, but how do we produce them?

FORMATION OF REDUCTION ATMOSPHERE

This can be done by putting into the kiln sufficient highly organic material to burn up most of the oxygen in the kiln atmosphere, thus leaving little or none at all for the pottery ware. By the term "highly organic" we refer to any material which has a high carbon content and which demands a lot of oxygen to burn it away completely into carbon monoxide or carbon dioxide gas. Charcoal obviously has a very high carbon content but there are also several other materials that potters could use. Some people use moth balls but although these produce a reduction atmosphere very efficiently, the gases given off tend to make the kiln very dirty inside and there appears to be some evidence of a gas being given off which results in a very slight glazing effect on the brickwork and elements. Reduction atmospheres, of course, are usually needed only to produce a special reduction effect in the glaze so that certain colours can be obtained. These colours are more or less "fixed" in the fired glaze at temperatures below about 750°C, as the glaze is then virtually rigid; a reduction atmosphere below this point is, therefore, not required. The glaze constituents are in their most reactive state and thus most susceptible to the effects of a reduction atmosphere when the glaze is at high temperature and in a molten condition. To achieve a maximum reduction effect it is consequently necessary to introduce the carbonaceous material into the kiln shortly after the glaze begins to melt and to continue additions at regular intervals until the kiln has reached the required firing temperature and has then been cooled down to about 750°C. This degree of reduction is, however, usually neither necessary nor desirable and one can usually obtain sufficient reduction by commencing to add the carbonaceous material immediately after switching off the kiln, continuing additions until the ware has cooled to about 750°C.

This may all sound so very simple but in actual practice it is not very easy to introduce carbon into the kiln at these high temperatures as dropping in a lump of charcoal, for example, could easily damage the pots being glazed inside the kiln. Many potters, however, overcome this problem by placing a suitable receptacle at a suitable position in the kiln to catch the pieces of charcoal being dropped into it. Charcoal can be introduced either through the spy-hole or through the vent-hole at the top or back of the kiln. As we want to maintain a reduction atmosphere inside the kiln it is necessary to replace the vent plug or the spy-hole plug as soon as the charcoal has been safely lowered in. This will help to prevent the reduction atmosphere from leaking out. After about half an hour add more charcoal to the kiln.

Podmore's, incidentally, have developed a special reduction bung which they can fit as an optional extra to kilns during manufacture. This takes the form of a comparatively large brick containing a spy-hole which can be removed from the door of the kiln while the kiln is being fired. This "bung" has a receptacle built into it which can be loaded with charcoal and then inserted into the kiln—just like replacing the spy-hole bung. Podmore's recommend the use of two of these so that while the charcoal in one is being used up inside the kiln the other one can be loaded, so that rapid replacement can be made.

Usually the use of reduction is reserved for high-fired work with stoneware so as to obtain the special colours mentioned above. At low temperatures, and particularly when low-solubility or other lead-containing glazes are being used, a reduction atmosphere should be avoided, for the lead content of the glaze will be reduced, forming an unpleasant greyish black discoloration in the glaze.

Lustre glazes can be made by loading the glaze with a very high metal content and then using a reduction atmosphere to form a metallic lustre on the surface of the glaze.

The characteristic colours produced in glazes by reduced forms of certain materials cannot be obtained by adding these materials already in reduced form to a glaze followed by a normal oxidizing firing. Red copper oxide cannot, for example, be added to a glaze followed by a normal firing in an attempt to achieve the characteristic copper red colour obtained in a reduction firing. During the normal firing the red copper oxide would be oxidized and one would obtain the usual copper-green-coloured glaze.

15 Some Pottery Faults and How to Overcome Them

Most pottery faults are caused by incorrect making procedures, incorrect materials or ignorance on the part of the potter. However, many of these defects can be influenced to a very considerable degree by adjusting the firing conditions or the firing cycle to which the ware is subjected—and some faults are indeed caused by incorrect firing procedures.

In this chapter are listed some of the common faults which will befall even the best of potters from time to time. They have been included in this book because when these problems occur it is important for the potter to determine how to overcome them and to decide what role the kiln can play in their cause and correction. Many pottery faults are often wrongly attributed to incorrect heat treatment in the kiln.

CRAZING

Crazing takes the form of very fine cracks spread throughout the glaze but especially in those areas that are more thickly glazed than others. These cracks permit moisture to enter into the body if this is porous, and this is, of course, unhygienic. For pottery which is used purely decoratively rather than functionally crazing can, however, be regarded as a decoration and can give an attractive appearance if the crazing is spread uniformly over the pottery.

The fundamental cause of both crazing and peeling is a difference in the degree of contraction of the body and of the glaze covering it. If the coefficients of expansion (by this we refer to the degree of expansion and contraction) of the body and of the glaze were exactly the same, crazing and peeling would never occur as a result of the firing operation. However, when pottery is being used it is often heated and cooled—especially when it is used as a receptacle for hot food and then subsequently washed in hot water. When this happens the first part of the pottery to be affected by the heat will be the surface, the heat gradually soaking through to the interior of the body. The glaze will therefore expand or contract a little sooner than the body, and these stresses could cause crazing. Glasses and glazes, however, can withstand far more compression than tension without cracking. This is to say that they can withstand being squeezed, without giving way, much more easily than they could withstand the same force trying to pull the glaze apart. It follows then that suddenly chilling a hot pottery surface is much more likely to cause the glaze to crack than suddenly heating it. This characteristic of glasses and glazes to withstand compressive forces more easily than tensile ones is used by ceramists to prevent crazing from occurring by deliberately attempting to put the glaze film into a state of compression. When pottery ware is then heated the glaze is compressed still further but the cooling operation, instead of putting the glaze into tension, merely results in a reduction of the compressive forces present in the glaze.

We have seen from an earlier chapter that the formation of cristobalite in the body is due to the body being fired to comparatively high temperatures and that this formation takes place slowly and results from the conversion of silica in the body. I have also shown that cristobalite contracts very sharply at about 225°C when being cooled and expands again at the same point when being heated. Pottery bodies containing cristobalite therefore contract rather sharply when being cooled when a temperature of about 225°C is reached. When a glaze is applied to a pottery body and subsequently fired in the glost kiln, the body, with the glaze covering it, contracts once the kiln has been switched off and cooling begins. The glaze at this stage, however, is molten and will therefore absorb any stresses or strains set up by the gradual contraction of the body. The glaze will gradually become more and more viscous as the temperature drops and will remain in a semi-fluid condition down to about 750°C. As cooling continues below this temperature the glaze becomes solid and can no longer absorb any stresses and strains as it could when in a semi-molten condition. When a temperature of 225°C or thereabouts is reached the body very rapidly contracts (because of the rapid contraction of cristobalite) and this has the effect of putting the glaze into compression. This compression remains in the glaze when the ware is taken from the kiln.

It will therefore be seen that crazing occurs when there is not sufficient compressive stress in the glaze and the glaze is subsequently heated and cooled. If cristobalite has not been allowed to develop properly in the body then there may be little or no compression in the glaze and crazing will take place very

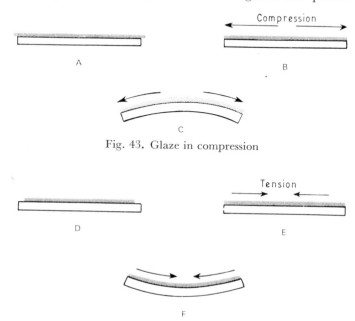

Fig. 43. Glaze in compression

Fig. 44. Glaze in tension

easily. I have mentioned that cristobalite is formed gradually by the conversion of silica and that this takes place when pottery is fired at comparatively high temperatures. If, therefore, one fires the biscuit ware to a low temperature, lower than that recommended, and then uses a glaze firing to a low temperature, there is likely to be insufficient cristobalite formation to prevent the glaze from subsequently crazing.

This may all sound a little complex and Figs. 43–4 (*A* to *F*) should be referred to as a summary. *A* shows a slab of biscuit ware of high expansion and contraction on which has been placed a glaze having a lower rate of expansion and contraction. The glaze wants to spread itself out over a greater surface than that offered by the biscuit slab. By firing the two together we arrive at *B* where both glaze and body occupy the same area and the glaze is in a state of compression. If the body was very thin or elastic this compression would relieve itself by the glaze forcing the body to bend (*C*). *D* illustrates a glaze having a higher expansion and contraction than that of the body which, when fired together, results in *E* where the glaze is being stretched by the body in an attempt to cover it. This is the condition of tension in which crazing can occur so easily. The glaze tension tries to relieve itself by bending the body as in *F*, which is the opposite of *C*.

The most common cause of crazing is through not firing the pottery to a high enough temperature or, if the pottery is fired to this temperature, not allowing enough time for the heat to really soak into the ware. Crazing can also be caused by applying the glaze far too thickly. Crazing is also caused by adding to the glaze, materials which have a very high coefficient of expansion. Some of the biggest offenders in this respect are soda (Na_2O), potash (K_2O), and most other alkali compounds. Alkaline glazes tend to contain comparatively high amounts of these oxides and this is why they seldom develop as much crazing resistance as other glazes.

It is obviously possible to affect crazing resistance by changing the composition or type of body. Generally speaking, the finer the particle size of the material, the more reactive it becomes. If the silica present in pottery bodies is not ground finely enough less cristobalite will tend to be formed.

Silica can be added to a porous body to increase the expansion by forming more cristobalite and yet can be added to the glaze to decrease expansion. In a glaze silica is converted to silicate which has a low expansion. Adding silica to either or both the glaze and the body can therefore help to overcome crazing.

Incidentally, pure silica will not form cristobalite until a temperature of 1450°C has been reached, but in the presence of felspar, stone, whiting, dolomite, talc, and also iron oxide, cristobalite may form at temperatures as low as 900 to 950°C. Talc tends to have a marked effect in this respect but it has to be imported and for this reason it is not often used in England.

Porous bodies will continually absorb moisture from the atmosphere causing them to swell. This can reach the stage where the expansion of the body releases all the compression

Fig. 45 Crazing

in the glaze and the glaze then goes into tension which, as the body continues to swell results in crazing. This is often seen on industrial tiles used in bathrooms or kitchens, after they have been in use for a considerable period of time.

PEELING

Peeling is the reverse of crazing and is caused by the glaze having far too much compression. Peeling appears as very fine cracks in the glaze the edges of which tend to ride over one another, i.e. overlap. It tends to take place particularly on the edges of pottery such as the top rim of cups. The sharp edges of glaze can be felt with the hand and often break away. Peeling is usually due to using a clay having too high a coefficient of expansion and/or a glaze not having a high enough coefficient.

This is, incidentally, a comparatively uncommon fault. Ways to overcome it include reducing the biscuit and glost firing temperature or adding to the glaze a material which has a high coefficient of expansion such as an alkaline frit.

CRAWLING

This is the name given to the tendency of the glaze to roll away from certain areas of the pottery after firing, leaving behind a bare patch of biscuit ware. It is generally caused by the presence on the biscuit ware before dipping, of oil, grease, or

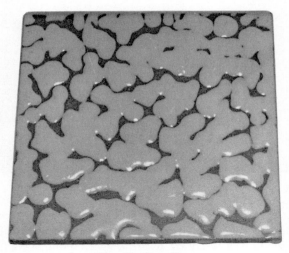

Fig. 46. Crawling

deposits of dust or similar materials. These either allow the glaze to run away from the affected area during the dipping operation or result in a very poor bond between the glaze and the body, allowing the glaze to roll away during the firing operation. It is, however, also commonly caused by knocking or otherwise damaging the unfired glaze surface. This again may result in the bond between the biscuit and the glaze film being broken, which results in the dislodged portion of glaze falling away from the pot when in the kiln, or in this portion melting with the rest of the glaze film and then being pulled away by surface tension.

Another common cause of crawling is the addition of materials to the glaze which will cause a considerable shrinkage of the glaze layer as this dries out after the glaze application process. Siccatives or "binders" such as starch, Courlose, Kirkose, Cellofas, gum arabic, gum tragacanth, etc., will all cause high shrinkage rates as also will excess additions of clays—for example, china clay and bentonite. Most of the binders are of a vegetable nature and will ferment if the liquid glaze is allowed to stand for several days or weeks—particularly in hot weather; if this is likely add a little formaldehyde to the glaze.

Other possible causes of crawling are—

(*a*) Soluble salts in the body causing a deposit on the surface of the ware in which case barium carbonate should be added to the body.

(*b*) Soluble salts present in the water supply used when "sponging" the ware or when "throwing" pots on the wheel. This can be cured by adding a little vinegar to the water.

(*c*) Glaze applied too thickly.

(*d*) Glaze applied when ware is not at the correct degree of dryness—especially with once-fired ware.

(*e*) Thick and thin sections of ware.

CUT GLAZE

This is another form of crawling and generally results from the glazed surface being scratched or otherwise marked after dipping. When the ware is fired, cut glazes show as a bare streak of biscuit showing through the glaze in the same position as the damage caused to the unfired glaze film. A thin smear of oil or grease can also give the same sort of effect and because of this there is often some confusion between crawling and cut glaze.

SCUMMING

This is due to the presence of soluble salts in the body and these in turn are generally introduced into the body from the water supply. What happens is that as the body dries after the pottery has been made, the water escaping from the body brings the soluble salts with it and since these cannot be vaporized into the atmosphere they are left behind on the surface of the pottery as a fine scum or powder which can sometimes be felt with the finger. For some reason this scum tends to be deposited around the edges of pottery such as the top rim of a cup.

The effect is to result in either the glaze running away from the scummed portion after dipping, or, more commonly, by the glaze flaking away from this area after firing.

It is a surprisingly common fault and can be overcome by converting the soluble salts present in the body into an insoluble form so that the moisture content of the body does not carry the salts with it when the water is being evaporated during drying. The usual method to convert soluble salts to insoluble ones is to add about 1–2½ per cent of barium carbonate to the body.

Soluble salts are more likely to be troublesome where water is taken from a static tank. When this happens the proportion of soluble salts in the tank water tends to increase because of loss of water by evaporation but not of the soluble salts dissolved in the water.

Incidentally, it is not unknown for the normal mains water supply in certain areas to contain a comparatively high proportion of soluble salts which may precipitate scumming on large pieces or cause difficulty in preparing casting slips to the recommended recipe.

DUNTING

This is the name given to a crack which generally passes completely through the pot, i.e. through both glaze and body, and is caused by thermal shock or stress. The line of fracture of a dunt is nearly always a gently curved one and has no sharp corners.

It is usually possible to tell whether a dunt has occurred when pottery is being heated in the kiln or whether it occurred in the cooling operation by inspecting the edges of the crack.

If a dunt occurred when the pottery was being heated, the edges of the crack will be rounded as the glaze subsequently melted during the firing operation. If the dunt occurred during the cooling operation then the edges will be sharp and the dunt may be very difficult to see.

Dunts hardly ever occur during the biscuit fire process, being largely confined to the glost fire and particularly to the

Fig. 47. Dunting

cooling cycle. They can be caused by having too much flint present in the body, the dunt then occurring usually at either the quartz or cristobalite inversions. The usual cause, however, is either trying to cool the kiln too quickly or trying to take pots out of the kiln before they are cool enough. In the desire to inspect the finished ware, discretion is too often cast to the winds and the kiln opened too soon. The results can be disastrous. As has been mentioned in the chapter on glost firing, the kiln can be cooled fairly quickly down to about 750°C and indeed this is normally desirable. Below about 750°C however, the kiln should be cooled progressively slower and pots should not be taken from the kiln until they can be handled with the bare hand.

There are other factors which can give rise to a tendency to dunting during the glost fire. Pots which are fairly thick at the base and have a much thinner cross-section near the top may often dunt when the base of the pot is placed flat upon the kiln shelf. When the kiln is fired the bottom of the pot takes considerably longer to heat up than the top; this gives rise to a stress between the top and the bottom of the pot which may in turn lead to a dunt. If you are firing pots of this nature try supporting them on stilts or saddles so that there is a gap between the base of the pot and the kiln shelf.

Some bodies are specially prepared to fire satisfactorily at earthenware temperatures of 1100 to 1150°C, but can also be fired at stoneware temperatures. The manufacturer sometimes adds cristobalite to these bodies to give satisfactory crazing resistance at the lower temperature but cristobalite naturally formed in the body at the higher temperatures can result in an excess of cristobalite, which can cause dunting. With bodies of this type used for stoneware it is best to fire the glost firing as rapidly as possible consistent with obtaining a satisfactory glazed surface.

Other possible causes are—

(*a*) Ware made with curves of too sharp radius—particularly on rim or foot of bowls.

(*b*) Thick and thin sections of ware.

(*c*) Overfiring.

CRACKING

Many cracks present in a piece of pottery immediately after making may not be noticeable to the naked eye. The biscuit firing however, will certainly make these open up and if cracks, particularly along the edges or rims of pottery pieces, are found when these pieces are withdrawn from the kiln the cause can usually be attributed to cracks present in the clay before firing. This in turn may be due to rapid or uneven drying, trimming clay with a blunt knife, or using a clay that is too short, i.e. not plastic enough, etc.

If, however, the kiln is fired too quickly over the "water smoking" period the moisture escaping from the clay may not be able to come out quickly enough and steam generated inside the pottery ware may reach such a pressure that it has to burst its way through. When this happens the pottery either cracks or may literally explode.

Incidentally, if any pieces are hollow they should be drilled with a small hole when the clay ware is in the "green" or "leather hard" state. If this is not done the air trapped inside the pot will expand when heated in the kiln and very likely blow the pot apart.

PINHOLED GLAZE

This is usually a body defect and not due to glaze. A very common cause is not firing the clay ware to a high enough biscuit temperature, followed by a glost firing at a higher temperature than the biscuit one. During the glost firing gas bubbles generated within the biscuit pottery then burst their way through the glaze surface, causing deep pinholes. Try firing the biscuit ware to a slightly higher temperature but do not exceed the maturing temperature of the clay.

With cast pottery, pinholes can easily be caused by introducing air bubbles into the casting slip—usually by a too vigorous mixing. The industrial practice is to keep the prepared casting slip under slow agitation in a large tank or "ark," during which time the pinholes trapped in the slip slowly escape to the surface. Air bubbles can also be forced into incorrectly wedged or incorrectly pugged clay. Finishing the clay ware with a damp sponging operation will usually smooth out any craters present on the surface of the pot and lend itself to a smoother glaze surface. However, avoid the use of excess water or very dirty water, for this can also lead to pinholing problems.

Other possible causes of pinholing are—

(a) Casting pottery in dirty or very old moulds. (Similarly the first cast or two in new moulds may give trouble).

(*b*) The addition of too much dry scraps from previous casting operations to the slip.

(*c*) Underglaze colour applied too heavily causes pinholes over the painted area.

(*d*) If making your own clay by a dry mix method be certain of obtaining a thorough mixing of the ingredients.

(*e*) Soluble salts in body.

(*f*) Ware not dry before dipping—especially biscuit ware.

(*g*) Excessive agitation of the glaze, thus forcing air bubbles into it.

Finally, as I have mentioned in Chapter 13, it is best to "soak" the glost firing for a period of about half an hour or so at the maximum firing temperature, as this allows the glaze more time to flow and thus fill in any pinholes or craters formed in it. If pinholing still persists and these appear to be due to the glaze then use a longer soaking temperature and cool the glaze more slowly if possible down to about 750°C.

DEVITRIFICATION

Occasionally when pottery is taken from the glost kiln it is found that the transparent glaze has turned a little milky—particularly where the glaze is most thickly applied. This milkiness occasionally takes on a pinkish or purplish discoloration when the transparent glazes are used over red bodies. This fault is referred to as devitrification.

It is generally caused by crystallization taking place in the glaze, forming calcium and zinc silicates or calcium borate. This crystallization takes place when the kiln is being cooled and while the glaze is still comparatively molten. Once the temperature of the kiln drops to below about 750°C the glaze is normally solid and no further devitrification can take place. The longer the time taken to cool the kiln down to this temperature the greater will be the danger of devitrification and the kiln should therefore be cooled fairly quickly over this temperature range.

Calcium borate is formed by a reaction between calcium present in the body and borax present in the glaze. It therefore follows that those glazes low in borax will tend to form less calcium borate. Leadless glazes generally contain far more borax than low-solubility types and devitrification is consequently much less likely to occur with the low-solubility type of glaze.

If the biscuit fire is fired to a temperature at least as high as that of the subsequent glost fire the biscuit ware will tend to become comparatively non-reactive during the glost fire and calcium cannot be leached out so easily, thus decreasing the likelihood of calcium borate formation.

To summarize the position: to overcome devitrification, firstly cool the kiln more quickly from switching off down to about 750°C, after which, of course, the kiln should be cooled at the normal slower rate to prevent dunting (i.e. cracking) taking place. Try firing the biscuit ware to higher temperatures—higher than the glaze if possible and, should the trouble still persist, which is unlikely, try using low-solubility glazes instead of leadless ones.

MATT GLAZES BECOME GLOSSY

Glossy glazes are changed to matt ones by the addition of materials which have the effect of raising the maturing temperature of the glaze with the result that the glaze is immature and matt when fired at the temperature normally used for the glossy glaze. Overfiring the glaze is consequently a very common cause of matt glazes firing to a glossy finish.

The matt effect of some glazes is imparted by the development of fine crystals formed in the glaze but a very rapid cooling can prevent these crystals from being developed in sufficient quantity to produce the matt finish. However, studio electric kilns generally cool comparatively slowly (provided the vent plug is left in position), and so a rapid cool is seldom responsible.

BLOW-OUT

This is the name given to a crater formed in the body by a piece of material being literally blown away from the surface. If the piece of ware has been glazed, the piece blown out will, of course, take a portion of the glaze with it, but this fault is usually confined to biscuit ware.

It is caused by the presence in the body of foreign particles, which give off gases fairly suddenly that generate so much pressure inside the body that they burst a small part of the pottery away at the surface thus relieving the pressure. Common potters' plaster is a very likely cause of this and if you are mixing scrap clay from your moulds with your working clay then you should make sure that you are not introducing plaster into the body. Minute specks of plaster will generally not cause any trouble but small nodules will.

This fault is also far more likely to occur with natural clays dug from the ground and used for pottery making, as these obviously contain a far higher portion of impurities than the prepared bodies sold by manufacturers.

SULPHURING

This appears as a dull scum or discoloration on the surface of the glaze. In very slight cases it may be possible to rub this scum away with the fingers but usually it remains as a permanent effect.

As the name implies, this fault is due to the interaction of sulphur gases present in the kiln atmosphere, with the glaze. These sulphur gases can arise in several different ways and can be introduced into the kiln from the products of combustion of oil, gas, and solid fuels, as well as being one of the normal gases given off by most pottery clays during the firing operation. Some clays and glazes contain considerably more sulphur compounds than others and to prevent sulphuring taking place these gases should be allowed to escape easily from the kiln. The usual way to overcome sulphuring is therefore to let the kiln cool a little more quickly by allowing a little more ventilation which at the same time lets the sulphur gases escape and reduces the length of time the pottery is in the kiln and thus open to attack.

With the studio pottery technique of firing the biscuit ware to a fairly low temperature and then applying the glaze and firing to a higher temperature the body becomes reactive again during the glost fire once the temperature of the biscuit fire has been passed. The sulphur gases coming away from the clay can then often cause sulphuring. Firing the biscuit fire to a higher temperature may consequently prevent this problem during the subsequent glost fire.

BLOATING

This fault is generally confined to the body and is nearly always due to overfiring. What happens is that when the body is over-fired the fluxes in the body begin to boil and the body becomes semi-molten. Gases formed by the boiling of the fluxes then

Fig. 48. Bloating

This is a section through a tile to show how the typical cavity has been formed inside the ware.

begin to blow bubbles inside the body with the result that small "lumps" appear all over the surface of the body. In extreme cases the body swells considerably and the writer has seen small tiles which are literally twice the size of tiles fired in the normal way.

BLISTERING

This is a similar fault to bloating but is the name given to blisters formed in the glaze. This again is generally due to the glaze being badly overfired so that boiling and bubbling takes place. These bubbles in the glaze usually break open as they burst leaving a crater which may show the biscuit ware underneath.

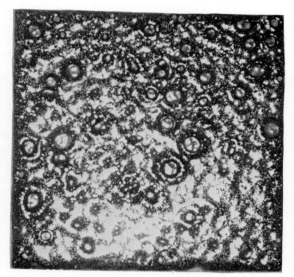

Fig. 49. Blistered glaze

The remedy is obvious. Either reduce the glost firing temperature or, if this is not possible, use glazes which have a higher firing range.

DULL UNDERGLAZE COLOURS

Underglaze colours are normally painted on to unglazed biscuit ware, which is then glazed when the colour has dried out. The glaze used should preferably be of the low-solubility type for these contain a certain proportion of lead which is compounded into the glaze in such a way that the risk of lead poisoning is negligible provided that elementary standards of hygiene are observed. This lead content of a low-solubility glaze produces a very glossy glaze and enhances very considerably the colour of any pigment applied in or under the glaze. By comparison leadless glazes produce colours which are dull and lifeless.

Most underglaze colours remain stable at temperatures up to about 1120 to 1150°C. At temperatures above this, many of them begin to change colour, become duller and burn away, although there are now a limited range of colours available which have been specially prepared to withstand stoneware temperatures up to 1300°C.

Underglaze colours are usually prepared for painting by mixing them with a special medium until the paint is of a suitable consistency. This medium contains a gum which can cause the glaze to "crawl" away from the colour to leave an area bare of glaze. To prevent this, industrial potters fire the painted, unglazed biscuit ware to a temperature of about 650°C. This "hardening-on" fire as it is called, serves to burn away the medium and at the same time fixes the painted design firmly to the pottery. The ware can then be dipped into glaze without risk of the glaze crawling away or smudging the painted design.

Underglaze colours can be painted on to the surface of the clay ware prior to biscuit firing or applied to the surface of unfired glazed ware. With the latter procedure it is best to mix some transparent glaze with the colour if a glossy colour is required as otherwise the colours will fire dull.

DULL ON-GLAZE COLOURS

On-glaze colours are normally mixed with an oil medium to allow them to be applied easily and when this is burned away during the firing operation the fumes given off must be allowed to escape easily or the quality of the colours will be affected very considerably. When firing on-glaze enamels the vent plug should be left partly open until the kiln interior has risen to about 350–400°C, or until the characteristic smell of burning oil medium can no longer be detected coming from the kiln. Not allowing these gases to escape is the usual cause of dull on-glaze colours.

Many colours, however, will become a little dull as a result of overfiring. On-glaze enamels should be fired at a temperature of about 730–750°C; at temperatures higher than this the colours (particularly reds) will begin to change their tone and to lose their gloss. If the temperature continued to rise beyond this point the colours would be burned away.

INACCURATE PYROMETER READINGS

An inaccurate reading on the pyrometer may be due to incorrect installation, in which case the Do's and Dont's listed on page 56 should be checked.

If the instrument temperature-indicating pointer does not move smoothly up and down the scale with gradual increase and decrease of temperature: if, for example, the pointer sticks at a particular setting and gently tapping the instrument causes the pointer to change to a different setting, then the instrument is definitely faulty and should be returned to the supplier.

Always remember that the temperature indicated by the collapse of Staffordshire cones, Holdcroft bars, etc., is at best a temperature approximation. These pyroscopes measure heat work and not true temperature as does a pyrometer and consequently a difference of 30°C or more between the reading on a pyrometer and the temperature suggested by the collapse of, for example, a Staffordshire cone, is quite common.

Appendix I

Cone No.	Degrees C	Degrees F	Cone No.	Degrees C	Degrees F	Cone No.	Degrees C	Degrees F
022	600	1110	02	1060	1940	12	1350	2460
022A	625	1155				13	1380	2515
021	650	1200	02A	1070	1960	14	1410	2570
020	670	1240	01	1080	1975			
			01A	1090	1995	15	1435	2615
019	690	1275	1	1100	2010	16	1460	2660
018	710	1310				17	1480	2695
017	730	1345	1A	1110	2030	18	1500	2730
016	750	1380	2	1120	2050			
			2A	1130	2065	19	1520	2770
015	790	1455	3	1140	2085	20	1530	2785
014	815	1500				26	1580	2875
013	835	1535	3A	1150	2100	27	1610	2930
012	855	1570	4	1160	2120			
			4A	1170	2140	28	1630	2965
011	880	1615	5	1180	2155	29	1650	3000
010	900	1650				30	1670	3040
09	920	1690	5A	1190	2175	31	1690	3075
08	940	1725	6	1200	2190			
			6A	1215	2220	32	1710	3110
08A	950	1740	7	1230	2245	33	1730	3145
07	960	1760				34	1750	3180
07A	970	1780	7A	1240	2265	35	1770	3220
06	980	1795	8	1250	2280			
			8A	1260	2300	36	1790	3255
06A	990	1815	8B	1270	2320	37	1825	3315
05	1000	1830				38	1850	3360
05A	1010	1850	9	1280	2335	39	1880	3415
04	1020	1870	9A	1290	2355			
			10	1300	2370	40	1920	3490
04A	1030	1885	10A	1310	2390	41	1960	3560
03	1040	1905				42	2000	3630
03A	1050	1920	11	1320	2410			

Fahrenheit temperatures are calculated from the centigrade figures and are shown to the nearest 5°.

Appendix II

Bar No.	Degrees C	Bar No.	Degrees C	Bar No.	Degrees C	Bar No.	Degrees C
1	600	11	890	22	1080	30	1325
2	650	12	905	23	1100	31	1350
3	670	13	920	24	1120	32	1380
4	700	14	935	25	1140	33	1430
5	730	15	950	25a	1170	34	1460
6	760	16	960	26	1200	35	1475
7	790	17	970	26a	1230	36	1490
7a	810	18	985	27	1250	37	1505
8	840	19	1000	27a	1270	38	1520
9	860	20	1040	28	1280	39	1535
10	875	21	1060	29	1300	40	1550

Appendix III

COLOUR OF FIRE/TEMPERATURE RELATIONSHIPS

Temp. °C	Approximate Staffordshire cone no.	Colour of fire	Effect on clay	Type of ware and glazes
225	—	No visible colour, i.e. "black heat"	Alpha to beta cristobalite inversion	
575	—		Alpha to beta quartz inversion	
600	022	Dull red		Firing temperature for on-glaze enamels (china paints)
750	016			
830	013			
850		Cherry red		Lustre glazes
875	011			
920	09		Most of organic matter burnt away by this time	
960	07	Cherry red/ orange		Low firing lead glazes sometimes opacified with tin oxide (majolica)
1000	05		Terracottas mature	Porous biscuit earthenware
1020	04			
1100	1	Orange changing to yellow/orange	Earthenware matures	Industrial earthenware biscuit and bone china glost
1150	3A			
1200	6	Distinct yellow orange	Terracottas melt. Increasing beta cristobalite formation	Semi-porcelain
1250	8			
1280	9	Slight white tinge		Salt glazes Bone china biscuit, stoneware and some porcelain
1300	10			
1350	12	White showing tinge of blue		Porcelain
1460	16			

131

Appendix IV

Podmore & Sons Ltd., Shelton, Stoke-on-Trent.

Cotton Bros, Crown Works, Portland Road, Longton, Stoke-on-Trent.

Kilns & Furnaces Ltd., Keele Street, Tunstall, Stoke-on-Trent.

Mills & Hubball Ltd., Victoria Rise, Clapham Common, London, S.W.4.

Fulham Pottery & Cheavin Filter Co. Ltd., 210 New Kings Road, Fulham, London, S.W.6.

Gibbons Bros. Ltd., Lenches Bridge, Brierley Hill, Staffs.

Applied Heat Co. Ltd., Elecfurn Works, Otterspool Way, Watford.

British Ceramic Services Co. Ltd., Bricesco House, Wolstanton, Newcastle-under-Lyme.

E. J. Arnold Ltd., Butterley Street, Leeds 10.

Cromartie Kilns Ltd., Dividy Road, Longton, Stoke-on-Trent.

Bernard W. E. Webber Ltd., Webcot Works, Alfred Street, Fenton, Stoke-on-Trent.

Shelley Furnaces Ltd., King Street, Longton, Stoke-on-Trent.

R. M. Catterson Smith Ltd., Adam Bridge Works, South Way, Wembley, Middx.

Wengers Ltd., Etruria, Stoke-on-Trent.

A. Gallenkamp & Co. Ltd., Technico House, Christopher Street, London, E.C.2.

Index

133